GCSE Maths Pocket Formula

GW00393165

CONTENTS

This Mathematics Pocket Formula Book was conceived after countless suggestions made by students for a comprehensive, easy-to-follow guide that covers all aspects of the syllabus. It covers all the Intermediate and Higher Tier topics set by all the Exam Boards.

This GCSE book gives students step-by-step methods to solve many maths problems, with valuable commentary and advice. It contains 'All you need to know', so any student with full knowledge of this pocket book should be well prepared for the GCSE exams.

Just remember, 'Maths is not difficult if you follow the rules.'

Published by HarperCollins*Publishers* Limited
77–85 Fulham Palace Road
Hammersmith London W6 8JB
www.**fire**and**water**.com

www.**Collins**Education.com
Online support for schools and colleges

© HarperCollins*Publishers* Limited 2002
First published 2002
Reprinted
10 9 8 7 6 5 4 3 2 1
ISBN 0 00 713419 3
Jeff Geha asserts the moral right to be identified as the author of this work.

British Library Cataloguing in Publication Data
A Catalogue record for this publication is available from the British Library

Edited by Joan Miller
Designed by Merlin Group International and Ann Miller
Artwork by Merlin Group International and Caroline Miller
Cover design by Susi Martin-Taylor
Printed in Great Britain by Martins the Printers Ltd, Berwick upon Tweed

Types of number

You need to be able to recognise the different types of number.

The main types are summarised in the table below.

Name	Description
Odd numbers	Numbers that end in 1, 3, 5, 7 or 9. They do not divide exactly by 2.
Even numbers	Numbers that end in 0, 2, 4, 6 or 8. They divide exactly by 2.
Multiples	Multiples of a number are found by multiplying the given number by the counting numbers (i.e. 1, 2, 3, 4, ...). For example, the multiples of 8 less than 45 are: $\{8 \times 1, 8 \times 2, 8 \times 3, 8 \times 4, 8 \times 5\}$ $= \{8, 16, 24, 32, 40\}$. The **lowest common multiple** (LCM) is the lowest number that is a common multiple of two or more numbers.
Factors	Factors of a number are those whole numbers that divide exactly into it. For example, factors of $20 = \{1, 2, 4, 5, 10, 20\}$. The **highest common factor** (HCF) is the highest number that is a common factor of two or more numbers.
Prime numbers	A prime number is any number that has only two factors, the number itself and one. Prime numbers less that 15 are $\{2, 3, 5, 7, 11, 13\}$. A **prime factor** is a factor that is also a prime number. Remember that 1 is not a prime number. It has only one factor.

Example

a Find the lowest common multiple (LCM) of 3 and 4.

b Find the highest common factor (HCF) of 12 and 18.

c Write 60 as a product of its prime factors.

Solution

a Multiples of 3:   3, 6, 9, **12**, 15, ...
   Multiples of 4:   4, 8, **12**, 16, 20, ...
   ∴ LCM = 12

b Factors of 12:   1, 2, 3, 4, **6**, 12
   Factors of 18:   1, 2, 3, **6**, 9, 18
   ∴ HCF = 6

c $60 = 2 \times 30 = 2 \times 2 \times 15 = 2 \times 2 \times 3 \times 5$

Directed numbers

Directed numbers have a sign (positive or negative) assigned to them. Directed whole numbers are also called **integers**. They include all positive and negative integers and zero. Directed numbers can be represented on a number line.

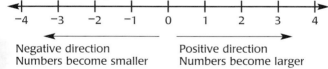

Negative direction   Positive direction
Numbers become smaller   Numbers become larger

Note: The larger the magnitude of a negative number, the smaller its value becomes. For example ⁻10 is smaller than ⁻5.

Adding and subtracting directed numbers

Step 1: If the question involves brackets, eliminate the brackets first as follows:

- two like signs (+ (+) or − (−)) become a positive (+)
- two unlike signs (+ (−) or − (+)) become a negative (−).

Step 2: Now, if the sign joining the numbers is:
- positive (+), move to the right.
- negative (−), move to the left.

Example

Use a number line to find the value of $^-2 - (^-4)$.

Solution

Step 1: $^-2 - (^-4) = ^-2 + 4$ (as $- (-) = +$)

Step 2: The sign joining the numbers is +.
∴ Start at $^-2$ and move 4 spaces right i.e. $^-2 + 4 = 2$.

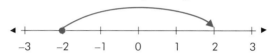

Multiplying and dividing directed numbers

Simply multiply or divide the two given numbers, and the final sign is obtained as follows.

- Two like signs become a positive (+)
  $+ \times +, \ - \times -, \ + \div +, \ - \div -$
- Two unlike signs become a negative (−)
  $+ \times -, \ - \times +, \ + \div -, \ - \div +$

Example

Find the value of: **a** $5 \times ^-4$ **b** $^-84 \div ^-7$.

Solution

a $5 \times ^-4 = ^+5 \times ^-4$ (Note: $+ \times - = -$)
            $= ^-20$

b $^-84 \div ^-7 = ^+12$ or 12 (Note: $- \div - = +$)

Metric units

Quantity	Unit	Conversion
Capacity	Cubic centimetre (cm³) Litre (*l*) Millilitre (m*l*)	1000 cm³ = 1 *l* 1000 mL = 1 *l* 1 cm³ = 1 m*l*
Length	Millimetre (mm) Centimetre (cm) Metre (m) Kilometre (km)	10 mm = 1 cm 100 cm = 1 m 1000 mm = 1 m 1000 m = 1 km
Mass	Gram (g) Kilogram (kg) Tonne (t)	1000 mg = 1 g 1000 g = 1 kg 1000 kg = 1 t

Imperial units

Quantity	Unit	Conversion
Capacity	Fluid ounces (fl oz) Pint (pt) Gallon (gall)	20 fl oz = 1 pt 8 pints = 1 gallon
Length	Foot Yard	1 foot = 12 inches 1 yard = 3 feet
Mass	Ounces (oz) Pounds (lb)	1 pound = 16 oz 1 stone = 14 lb

Conversions between metric and imperial units

Length	Mass	Capacity
2.5 cm ≈ 1 inch	25 g ≈ 1 ounce	1 litre ≈ $1\frac{3}{4}$ pints
30 cm ≈ 1 foot	**1 kg ≈ 2.2 pounds**	**4.5 litres ≈ 1 gallon**
1 m ≈ 39 inches		
8 km = 5 miles	You should memorise the conversions shown in **bold**.	

Note: The conversions are only approximate.

Decimal places

Decimal places are the positions of the digits after the decimal point in a decimal number. Follow these steps to write decimals correct to a given number of decimal places.

Step 1: Write down the initial calculator display in full before rounding.

Step 2: Rounding:
- If the value of the next digit is greater than or equal to 5, then round up (add 1 to the digit preceding it).
- If the value of the next digit is 4 or less, then round down (leave the digit preceding it as it is).

Example

Express 0.055 49 correct to:

a one decimal place.

b two decimal places.

c three decimal places.

d four decimal places.

Solution

a $0.055\,49 \approx 0.1$ (1 d.p.)   *(figure following 0 is 5)*

b $0.055\,49 \approx 0.06$ (2 d.p.)   *(figure following 5 is 5)*

c $0.055\,49 \approx 0.055$ (3 d.p.)   *(figure following 5 is 4, less than 5)*

d $0.055\,49 \approx 0.0555$ (4 d.p.) *(figure following 4 is 9, greater than 5)*

Note: On most scientific or graphics calculators, rounding can be done directly by pressing:

MODE 7 , followed by the number of decimal places you want.

e.g. to round off to 2 decimal places press:

MODE 7 2 .

Significant figures

The significant figures (s.f.) in a number are counted from the first non-zero digit. Zeros at the end are not counted as significant figures, but zeros within the non-zero digits are.

To round a number correct to a given number of significant figures, the steps are similar to those outlined for decimal places.

Example

Express 205.0475 correct to:

a 5 significant figures   **b** 2 significant figures.

Solution

a 205.0475 = 205.05 correct to 5 significant figures (5 s.f.).

b 205.0475 = 210 correct to 2 significant figures (2 s.f.).

Note: We rounded the zero up as the next digit was 5.
The zeros in the 'tens' and 'tenths' positions in the original number are significant.

Example

Express 0.009 63 correct to:

a 2 significant figures   **b** 1 significant figure.

Solution

a 0.009 63 = 0.0096 correct to 2 significant figures (2 s.f.).

b 0.009 63 = 0.01 correct to 1 significant figure (1 s.f.).

Note: When you give an answer that is rounded, you should always say how it is rounded, for example, 3 s.f. or 2 d.p.
You should try to aim for the same accuracy in your answer as the numbers given in the question, or follow the instructions in the question if any are stated.

Approximations

You may also be asked to make other kinds of approximation in certain questions. The examples below illustrate the different types of questions involving approximations.

Example

a Round 37.65 to the nearest whole number.

b Round 4.2655 to the nearest hundredth.

c Round 987 to the nearest ten.

Solution

a 37.65 is closer to 38 than 37
∴ 37.65 ≈ 38 to the nearest whole number.

b 4.2655 ≈ 4.27 to the nearest hundredth as the number following the 6 is equal to 5.

c 987 is closer to 990 than 980
∴ 987 ≈ 990 to the nearest ten.

Estimation and approximation

Quick estimates of calculations can prove very useful in daily life. Simply round the numbers to one significant figure, and then do the calculation.

In exams, to earn full marks, it is essential that you show all working when performing estimation.

Example

Estimate the value of $\dfrac{906 \times 38}{18\pi}$.

Solution

$$\frac{906 \times 38}{18\pi} \approx \frac{900 \times 40}{20 \times 3} = \frac{36\,000}{60} = 600$$

Note: π is taken as approximately 3.

Standard index form

Standard index form (SI form) or scientific notation is used to express very large or very small numbers more easily.

Standard form numbers are always written in the form:

$$A \times 10^n$$

where $1 \leqslant A < 10$ (A takes a value from 1 to 10) and n is a positive or negative whole number.

Note:

- n is positive for large numbers (e.g. $4.2 \times 10^3 = 4200$) and n is negative for small numbers (e.g. $5 \times 10^{-4} = 0.0005$)

- for positive n, move the digits n places left (to get a bigger number)
  for negative n, move the digits n places right (to get a smaller number)

- 10^2 is one hundred 10^3 is one thousand
  10^{-2} is one 100th 10^{-3} is one 1000th

On a scientific or graphics calculator, scientific notation correct to k significant figures is given by:

MODE [8] [k]

Note: Calculators are not all the same, so check how your calculator deals with standard form, *before* the exam.

Example

Express the following in standard index form correct to 2 significant figures.

a 0.006 57   **b** 953

Solution

a $0.006\,57 = 6.57 \times 10^{-3} = 6.6 \times 10^{-3}$ to 2 s.f.

b $953 = 9.53 \times 10^2 = 9.5 \times 10^2$ to 2 s.f.

Addition and subtraction

To add or subtract numbers expressed in standard index form follow these steps.

Step 1: If the powers are the same go to step 2. If not, multiply or divide one of the numbers by a power of 10, so that the powers are the same in both numbers.

Step 2: Add or subtract the digits then multiply by the power of 10.

Step 3: Convert your answer to standard form.

Multiplication and division

To multiply or divide numbers expressed in standard index form follow these steps.

Step 1: Multiply or divide the numbers and them multiply or divide the powers of 10 separately.

Step 2: **Add** the powers of 10 if you are multiplying and **subtract** the powers of 10 if you are dividing.

Step 3: Convert your answer to standard index form.

Using a calculator

You would normally complete standard index form calculations using a calculator as follows.

Step 1: Press MODE 8 first.

Step 2: Enter each number, using the EXP or EE key on your calculator.

e.g. to enter 4.56×10^9 press: $\boxed{4}$ $\boxed{\cdot}$ $\boxed{5}$ $\boxed{6}$ EXP $\boxed{9}$

Step 3: Complete the calculation. The answer will be given in standard index form.

Note: Again, check how to do this on your own calculator.

Example

Evaluate, giving your answer in standard index form.

a $(9.61 \times 10^4) - (7.29 \times 10^4)$ **b** $(3.35 \times 10^5) + (8.42 \times 10^6)$

c $(6.28 \times 10^3) \times (6.65 \times 10^8)$ **d** $(5.6 \times 10^4) \div (1.4 \times 10^7)$

Solution

a **Step 1:** The powers are the same, go to step 2.

Step 2: $(9.61 \times 10^4) - (7.29 \times 10^4)$
$= (9.61 - 7.29) \times 10^4$
$= 2.32 \times 10^4$

Step 3: 2.32×10^4

b **Step 1:** $(3.35 \times 10^5) + (8.42 \times 10^6)$
$= (3.35 \times 10^5) + (84.2 \times 10^5)$
Note: $8.42 \times 10^6 = 8.42 \times 10 \times 10^5 = 84.2 \times 10^5$

Step 2: $(3.35 + 84.2) \times 10^5 = 87.55 \times 10^5$

Step 3: $87.55 \times 10^5 = 8.755 \times 10^6$

c **Step 1:** $(6.28 \times 10^3) \times (6.65 \times 10^8)$
$= (6.28 \times 6.65) \times (10^3 \times 10^8)$
$= 41.762 \times 10^{11}$ *Add the powers.*

Step 2: $41.762 \times 10^{11} = 4.1762 \times 10^{12}$

d **Step 1:** $(5.6 \times 10^4) \div (1.4 \times 10^7)$
$= (5.6 \div 1.4) \times (10^4 \div 10^7)$
$= 4 \times 10^{-3}$ *Subtract the powers.*

Step 2: 4×10^{-3}

Note: Make sure you can perform the above calculations on your calculator as well.

Powers, roots and reciprocals

Powers	A number that is multiplied by itself one or more times is raised to a **power**.
Square numbers	A number raised to the power of 2 is **squared**. The square numbers are: 1, 4, 9, 16, 25, ... (1^2, 2^2, 3^2, 4^2, 5^2, ...)
Cube numbers	A number raised to the power of 3 is **cubed**. The cube numbers are: 1, 8, 27, 64, 125, ... (1^3, 2^3, 3^3, 4^3, 5^3, ...)
Square roots	Taking the square root (denoted by $\sqrt{}$) is the reverse operation to squaring a number. e.g. $7^2 = 49 \rightarrow \sqrt{49} = 7$
Cube roots	Taking the cube root (denoted by $\sqrt[3]{}$) is the reverse operation to cubing. e.g. $5^3 = 125 \rightarrow \sqrt[3]{125} = 5$
Reciprocals	The reciprocal of any non-zero number can be found by converting the number to a fraction and turning it upside-down. e.g. the reciprocal of 5 is $\frac{1}{5}$ e.g. the reciprocal of $\frac{2}{5}$ is $\frac{5}{2}$.

Indices

When a number is expressed in the form x^y, x is known as the **base** and y is known as the **index** or **power**. The base is the value which has to be multiplied and the index indicates how many times.

e.g. $5^4 = 5 \times 5 \times 5 \times 5 = 625$

The laws of indices

You **must** know these laws.

- $a^0 = 1$ *Any number to the power of 0 is 1.*
- $a^m \times a^n = a^{m+n}$ *The base is the same in both numbers.*
- $a^{-n} = \dfrac{1}{a^n}$ *Check by multiplying both sides by a^n.*

- $a^m \div a^n = a^{m-n}$ *The base is the same in both numbers.*

Notes:
- When **multiplying** like terms, **add** the indices.
- When **dividing** like terms, **subtract** the indices.
- Any number to the power of 0 is 1.

Example

Simplify, expressing your answer in standard index form where possible.

a $5^0 \times 2^2 \times 3^3$ **b** $4^{12} \div 4^7$ **c** $2 \times 2^2 \times 2^3 \times 2^4$

Solution

a $5^0 \times 2^2 \times 3^3 = 1 \times 4 \times 27 = 108$

b $4^{12} \div 4^7 = 4^{12-7} = 4^5$

c $2 \times 2^2 \times 2^3 \times 2^4 = 2^{1+2+3+4} = 2^{10}$

Fractions

Types of fraction

- In **improper fractions** (or top-heavy fractions) the numerator is larger than the denominator (e.g. $\frac{7}{5}$, $\frac{9}{4}$).

- **Mixed numbers** are made up of a whole number plus a fraction (e.g. $1\frac{2}{3}$, $3\frac{1}{2}$).

Equivalent fractions

These are fractions that have the same value. Given any fraction, you can find another equivalent fraction by multiplying or dividing both the numerator and the denominator by the same number.

e.g. $\frac{2}{5} \overset{\times 2}{\underset{\times 2}{=}} \frac{4}{10}$ $\frac{10}{15} \overset{\div 5}{\underset{\div 5}{=}} \frac{2}{3}$

Simplifying fractions

To simplify fractions as far as possible, divide the numerator and the denominator by their **highest common factor** (HCF). This is the highest number that will divide into both numbers.

e.g. $\frac{16}{20} \overset{\div 4}{\underset{\div 4}{=}} \frac{4}{5}$ (dividing top and bottom by 4 – the HCF of 16 and 20)

Using a calculator

- To **simplify** fractions:
  1 Enter the numerator.
  2 Press the a^b/c key.
  3 Enter the denominator.
  4 Press $=$.

- To **convert a mixed number** to an improper fraction:
  1 Enter the whole number.
  2 Press the a^b/c key.
  3 Enter the numerator.
  4 Press the a^b/c key.
  5 Enter the denominator.
  6 Press $\boxed{\text{SHIFT}}$ a^b/c .

13

Addition and subtraction

To add or subtract fractions first find a common denominator (bottom value), then use it to obtain equivalent fractions with the same denominator, then add or subtract the numerators.

To find the common denominator, find the lowest common multiple (LCM) of the denominators in the given fractions.

Example

Find $\frac{3}{5} + \frac{1}{3}$

Solution

The LCM of 5 and 3 is $5 \times 3 = 15$

so the lowest common denominator is 15.

$\therefore \frac{3}{5} + \frac{1}{3}$ becomes $\frac{9}{15} + \frac{5}{15}$

and $\frac{9}{15} + \frac{5}{15} = \frac{14}{15}$

Multiplication

Step 1: Change any mixed numbers to improper fractions.

Step 2: Multiply the numerators and multiply the denominators.

Step 3: Simplify the answer where possible.

Example

Find $3\frac{1}{5} \times 4\frac{1}{4}$

Solution

Step 1: $3\frac{1}{5} = 3 + \frac{1}{5} = \frac{15}{5} + \frac{1}{5} = \frac{16}{5}$

$\qquad\quad 4\frac{1}{4} = 4 + \frac{1}{4} = \frac{16}{4} + \frac{1}{4} = \frac{17}{4}$

Step 2: $\frac{16}{5} \times \frac{17}{4} = \frac{272}{20}$

Step 3: $\frac{272}{20} = 13\frac{12}{20} = 13\frac{3}{5}$

Division

Step 1: Change any mixed numbers to improper fractions.

Step 2: Change the division sign to a multiplication sign and multiply by the reciprocal of the fraction by which you are dividing (the one that follows the division sign).

Step 3: Multiply the numerators and multiply the denominators.

Step 4: Simplify the answer where possible.

Example

Find $\frac{2}{3} \div 1\frac{3}{8}$

Solution

Step 1: $1\frac{3}{8} = 1 + \frac{3}{8} = \frac{8}{8} + \frac{3}{8} = \frac{11}{8}$

Step 2: $\frac{2}{3} \div \frac{11}{8} = \frac{2}{3} \times \frac{8}{11}$

Step 3: $\frac{2}{3} \times \frac{8}{11} = \frac{16}{33}$

Step 4: $\frac{16}{33}$ cannot be simplified any further.

Expressing one quantity as a fraction of another

To express one quantity as a fraction of another:

● ensure that the units are same

● write the first value over the second value and cancel.

15

Percentages

Changing between percentages, fractions and decimals

Percentages, fractions and decimals are all types of fraction but are just written in different ways. To change:

- percentages to fractions: *Divide by 100.*

- percentages to decimals: *Divide by 100.*

- fractions to percentages: *Multiply by 100%.*

- decimals to percentages: *Multiply by 100%.*

Ordering numbers

When you need to arrange a set of percentages, fractions and decimals in order, it is best to change them all to percentages first.

Example

Place these numbers in descending order: $\frac{1}{2}$, 58%, 0.55, $\frac{3}{5}$

Solution

$\frac{1}{2} \times 100\% = 50\%$, $0.55 \times 100\% = 55\%$, $\frac{3}{5} \times 100\% = 60\%$

60%, 58%, 55%, 50%   *Place in descending order.*

$\frac{3}{5}$, 58%, 0.55, $\frac{1}{2}$ *Rewrite in original form.*

Finding a percentage of a quantity

To find the percentage of a quantity.

- express the percentage as a decimal (or fraction)

- then multiply by the quantity.

e.g. 90% of 1000 = 0.9 × 1000 = 900
     130% of 70 = 1.3 × 70 = 91

Expressing one quantity as a percentage of another

To express a quantity A, as a percentage of another quantity B, use:

$\dfrac{A}{B} \times \dfrac{100}{1}$

Example

a Find £9 as a percentage of £20.

b Express 42 minutes as a percentage of an hour.

Solution

a $\dfrac{9}{20} \times \dfrac{100}{1} = 45\%$

b 1 hour = 60 minutes

$\dfrac{42}{60} \times \dfrac{100}{1} = 70\%$

Increasing or decreasing by a given percentage

- To **increase** an amount by $x\%$, find:
  $(100 + x)\% \times$ the amount

- To **decrease** an amount by $x\%$, find:
  $(100 - x)\% \times$ the amount

Example

A shop buys shirts for £30 and marks them up by 70%.
What is the selling price of the shirts?

Solution

Increasing 30 by 70% = $(100 + 70)\% \times 30$
$= 170\% \times 30$
$= 1.7 \times 30$
$= £51$

Percentage change

To find how a quantity, such as a price, changes, use:

$$\text{percentage change} = \frac{\text{change in value}}{\text{original amount}} \times 100\%$$

Note: In problems about buying and selling, you may be asked to find percentage gain or percentage loss. If the 'new' price is greater than the 'old', it is a profit or gain, if the 'new' price is lower than the 'old', it is a loss.

Example

A car valued at £8000 is sold for £7000. What is the percentage loss?

Solution

$$\text{Percentage loss} = \frac{\text{change in value}}{\text{original amount}} \times 100\%$$

$$\text{Percentage loss} = \frac{1000}{8000} \times 100\% = 12.5\%$$

Using percentages to find the original value

If you are given a number or amount A that represents $x\%$ of a whole, the whole value, V, is given by:

$$V = \frac{A}{x} \times \frac{100}{1}$$

Example

After it has been discounted by 25%, the price of a book is £19.95. Find the original price of the book.

Solution

£19.95 represents 75% (100% − 25%) of the original value (V).

So $V = \dfrac{A}{x} \times \dfrac{100}{1} = \dfrac{19.95}{75} \times \dfrac{100}{1} = £26.60$

Ratios

A ratio is a comparison of two (or more) quantities in a definite order. The ratio of a to b is given by:

$a : b$ or $\dfrac{a}{b}$

Ratios can be simplified in the same way as fractions.

Dividing quantities in a given ratio

To divide a quantity in a given ratio, follow these steps.

Step 1: Add all the ratios to find the total number of shares.

Step 2: Find the value of one share by dividing the given quantity by the number of shares from step 1.

Step 3: Multiply the value of one share by the individual numbers in the ratio to find the different quantities.

Example

The ratio of green to red apples in a box is 3 : 5. If there are 24 apples in total, how many are green?

Solution

Step 1: Total number of shares or parts = 3 + 5 = 8

Step 2: 8 parts = 24 so 1 part = 3　　$(24 \div 8 = 3)$

Step 3: 3 parts = 3 × 3 = 9 so 9 apples are green.

Increasing or decreasing by a given ratio

Example

If you need 90 g of butter to bake a pie for six people, how much butter do you need for a pie for four people?

Solution

90 g are needed for six people
So 15 g are needed for one person　　$(90 \div 6 = 15)$
∴ 4 × 15 = 60 g of butter are needed for a pie for four people.

Compound measures

Speed, distance and time

The three formulae connecting speed, distance and time are:

- average speed = $\dfrac{\text{total distance}}{\text{total time}}$

- time = $\dfrac{\text{distance}}{\text{speed}}$

- distance = speed × time

Example

a A car travels 320 miles in 4 hours. Find its average speed.

b Jayne goes for a $1\frac{1}{2}$ hour brisk walk at the rate of 5 km/h.
How far has she travelled in that time?

Solution

a Average speed = $\dfrac{\text{total distance}}{\text{total time}} = \dfrac{320}{4} = 80$

∴ Average speed is 80 mph.

b Distance = speed × time = $5 \times 1\frac{1}{2} = 7.5$

∴ Jayne travelled a distance of 7.5 km.

Density

The three formulae connecting density, mass and volume are:

- density = $\dfrac{\text{mass}}{\text{volume}}$

- volume = $\dfrac{\text{mass}}{\text{density}}$

- mass = density × volume

Simple and compound interest

Simple interest

Simple interest is paid at a fixed rate, over a period of time. The amount invested does not change. The simple interest earned when investing (or borrowing) at a simple rate is given by:

$I = \dfrac{P \times R \times T}{100}$ and $A = P + I$

where: I = simple interest

P = principal or original investment

R = rate (% per annum)

T = time in years

A = total amount

Example

Find the simple interest earned if Emma invests £5000 at 5% p.a. for 2 years.

Solution

$P = 5000, R = 5, T = 2$

$I = \dfrac{P \times R \times T}{100} = \dfrac{5000 \times 5 \times 2}{100} = £500$

Compound interest

Compound interest is paid at a fixed rate, over a period of time, but the interest is added to the principal every time. The amount invested increases whenever interest is paid. The compound interest earned when investing (or borrowing) at a compound rate is given by:

$A = P \times (1 + \dfrac{R}{100})^T$

where: A = total amount

P = principal or original investment

R = rate (% per annum)

T = time in years

Example

What is the value of £3000 invested at 6% for 8 years?

Solution

$P = 3000$, $R = 6$, $T = 8$

$$A = P \times (1 + \frac{R}{100})^T = 3000 \times (1 + \frac{6}{100})^8$$

$$= 3000 \times (1.06)^8$$

$$= £4781.54 \text{ (to the nearest penny)}$$

Note: When working with questions involving money, round your answer to 2 decimal places.

Personal and household finance

Wages and salaries

- A **salary** is a fixed amount of money earned per year, usually paid fortnightly or monthly.
- A **weekly wage** is paid at a fixed hourly rate.
- **Overtime** rates are paid for hours worked outside the normal working day. The rate for overtime hours is often 'time and a half' (1.5 × normal rate) or 'double time' (2 × normal rate).

Value added tax (VAT)

VAT is a tax that is added to the cost of most goods and services.

Example

A hotel charges £115 per night. VAT is charged at 17.5%. Find the price of one night's accommodation.

Solution

VAT = 17.5% of £115 = $\frac{17.5}{100} \times 115 = £20.13$

Final price = 115 + 20.13 = £135.13

Hire purchase (HP)

This is a method that allows consumers to purchase goods by paying an initial deposit and then paying the balance in monthly or weekly installments over a period of time.

To calculate the amount of each installment follow these steps.

Step 1: Calculate the initial deposit.
Deposit = percentage rate × cash price

Step 2: Calculate the balance owing (P).
P = cash price − deposit

Step 3: Calculate the interest to be paid on the balance owing (P).
$$I = \frac{P \times R \times T}{100}$$

Step 4: Calculate the total amount owed by the customer. ($P + I$).

Step 5: Divide ($P + I$) by the number of installments to find the value of each payment.

Example

Sonya bought a lounge suite (cash price £2800) by paying a 25% deposit and then paying the balance in monthly installments over $1\frac{1}{2}$ years. Interest of 10% was charged on the balance owing.

Calculate the amount of each payment.

Solution

Step 1: Deposit = percentage rate × cash price
= 25% × £2800 = 0.25 × £2800
= £700

Step 2: P = cash price − deposit
= £2800 − £700 = £2100

Step 3: $I = \dfrac{P \times R \times T}{100} = \dfrac{2100 \times 10 \times 1.5}{100}$ = £315

Step 4: Total amount owed = $P + I$ = £2100 + £315 = £2415

Step 5: Monthly payment = $\dfrac{£2415}{18}$ = £134.17

23

Rational and irrational numbers

A **rational** number is one that can be expressed in the form $\frac{p}{q}$ where p and q are integers (e.g. $\frac{1}{5}$, 0.3).

An **irrational** number is one that cannot be expressed in the form $\frac{p}{q}$ where p and q are integers (e.g. $\sqrt{2}$, π).

Irrational numbers involving square roots are known as **surds**. You need to be familiar with the following properties of surds in both the forward and reverse directions.

- $\sqrt{a} \times \sqrt{a} = a$
- $\sqrt{a} \times \sqrt{b} = \sqrt{ab}$
- $a\sqrt{b} + c\sqrt{b} = (a + c)\sqrt{b}$
- $a\sqrt{b} \times c\sqrt{b} = ac\sqrt{b^2} = acb$
- $\sqrt{a^2 b} = \sqrt{a^2} \times \sqrt{b} = a\sqrt{b}$

Recurring decimals

A recurring decimal is a decimal in which one digit, or group of digits, is repeated. Recurring decimals are all rational numbers as they can be expressed as fractions.

To convert recurring decimals to fractions follow these steps.

Step 1: Let x = recurring decimal in expanded form.

Step 2: Let the number of recurring digits = n
(e.g. in $0.\dot{3}$, $n = 1$, in $0.1\dot{2}\dot{3}$ $n = 2$)

Step 3: Multiply the whole of the recurring decimal by 10^n.

Step 4: Subtract (1) from (3) to eliminate the recurring part.

Step 5: Solve for x, expressing your answer as a fraction in its simplest form.

Example

Express $0.12\dot{5}$ as a fraction in its simplest form.

Solution

Step 1: Let $x = 0.125\,252\,5...$.

Step 2: $n = 2$

Step 3: Multiply x by $10^2 = 100$.
$$100x = 12.525\,25...$$

Step 4: Subtract (1) from (3).
$$99x = 12.4$$

Step 5: From (4), $99x = 12.4$
$$990x = 124 \qquad \text{Multiply by 10.}$$
$$x = \frac{124}{990} = \frac{62}{495}$$

Fractional indices

Fractional indices involve roots of the base numbers.

$$a^{\frac{1}{2}} = \sqrt{a}, \quad a^{\frac{1}{3}} = \sqrt[3]{a}, \quad a^{\frac{1}{n}} = \sqrt[n]{a}, \quad a^{\frac{m}{n}} = (a^{\frac{1}{n}})^m = (\sqrt[n]{a})^m$$

- $4^{\frac{1}{2}} = \sqrt{4} = 2$
- $27^{\frac{2}{3}} = (27^{\frac{1}{3}})^2 = (\sqrt[3]{27})^2 = (3)^2 = 9$

Proportion

- If y is proportional to x then you can write:
  $y \propto x$ or $y = kx$
- If y is inversely proportional to x then you can write:
  $y \propto \dfrac{1}{x}$ or $y = \dfrac{k}{x}$

where k is a constant multiplier and is called the **constant of proportionality**.

Upper and lower bounds

If the length of a table is given as 4 m to the nearest metre, then the actual length (l) will lie in the interval:

$3.5 \leqslant l < 4.5$

The value 3.5 is known as the *lower bound* and 4.5 is known as the *upper bound*.

Note: The upper bound approaches 4.5 but can never get there, because if it did the number would be rounded up. Hence the < symbol is used at the upper bound.

Example

A wall 5.6 m long by 2.4 m high is to be painted. The instructions on the tin of paint state that 1 litre of paint will cover 11 m^2. Find the maximum amount of paint required, assuming that all the given measurements are correct to 2 significant figures.

Solution

First you need to find the upper bound for the area of the wall.

Upper bound = $5.65 \times 2.45 = 13.8425$ m^2

The lower bound for the area covered by 1 litre of paint is 10.5 m^2.

The maximum amount of paint required is given by:

$$\text{maximum paint required} = \frac{\text{maximum area of wall}}{\text{maximum coverage}}$$

$$= \frac{13.8425}{10.5}$$
$$= 1.134 \text{ litres to 3 d.p.}$$

A **sequence** is a set of numbers that follows a certain rule.

- If the terms in the sequence of the differences between successive terms are constant then a linear rule applies. i.e. the nth term is given by
  $an + b$

- If the terms in the sequence of the differences of the differences (the second differences) are constant then a quadratic rules applies. i.e. the nth term is given by
  $an^2 + bn + c$

where a, b, c are integers and n is the position of the term in the sequence.

Example

Find the nth term of this sequence: 6, 9, 14, 21, 30, ...

Solution

As the difference of the differences is constant, then a quadratic rule applies. Construct a table.

Term (n)		1	2	3	4	5
Sequence	(1)	6	9	14	21	30
Try n^2	(2)	1	4	9	16	25
Difference (1) − (2)		5	5	5	5	5

The difference is always equal to 5, so try adding 5 to the terms in (2) to form a sequence.

Try $n^2 + 5$		6	9	14	21	30

This gives the sequence we are looking for.

So the nth term is $n^2 + 5$.

Interpreting graphs of real-life situations

You need to be familiar with interpreting graphs of different real-life situations.

Example

The graph below represents the journey of a car from town A to town B.

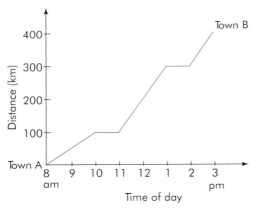

a When and for how long did the car stop?

b What was the average speed for the whole trip?

Solution

a The car stopped at 10:00 a.m. and at 1:00 p.m.
It stopped for 1 hour each time.

b Average speed = $\dfrac{\text{total distance travelled}}{\text{total time taken}} = \dfrac{400}{7} = 57.1$ km/h

Linear graphs

Graphs of straight lines

The word 'linear' means 'in a straight line'. To draw the graph of a straight line, follow these steps.

Step 1: Set up a table of values, typically $x = 0, 1, 2$, and find their equivalent y-values.

Step 2: Plot the points.

Step 3: Join the points with a straight line.

Gradient and y-intercept ($y = mx + c$)

$$\text{Gradient} = \frac{\text{vertical distance}}{\text{horizontal distance}}$$

$$= \frac{\text{change in } y}{\text{change in } x}$$

Note: A **positive** gradient means the line slopes **up**, a **negative** gradient means the line slopes **down**.

All linear graphs (with the exception of vertical lines) can be written in the form:

$$y = mx + c$$

Note: m is the gradient and c is the y-intercept.

Example

Write down the equations of the lines shown.

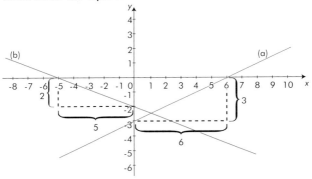

Solution

a Gradient = $\dfrac{\text{change in } y}{\text{change in } x} = \dfrac{3}{6} = \dfrac{1}{2}$

As the line slopes up the gradient is positive.

The y-intercept is $^-3$.

$\therefore$ the equation of the line is $y = \dfrac{1}{2}x - 3$

b Gradient = $\dfrac{\text{change in } y}{\text{change in } x} = \dfrac{2}{5}$

As the line slopes down the gradient is negative.

The y-intercept is $^-2$.

$\therefore$ the equation of line is $y = -\dfrac{2}{5}x - 2$

Quadratic, cubic and reciprocal graphs

You need to be familiar with the following basic curves and any slight variations on them.

Quadratic

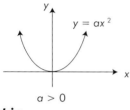

$y = ax^2$

$a > 0$

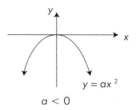

$y = ax^2$

$a < 0$

Cubic

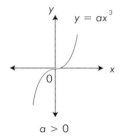

$y = ax^3$

$a > 0$

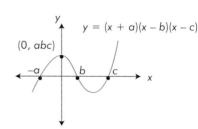

$y = (x + a)(x - b)(x - c)$

$(0, abc)$

$-a$ b c

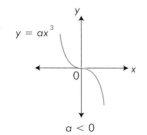

$y = ax^3$

$a < 0$

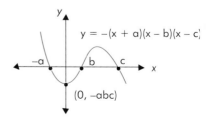

$y = -(x + a)(x - b)(x - c)$

$-a$ b c

$(0, -abc)$

Reciprocal

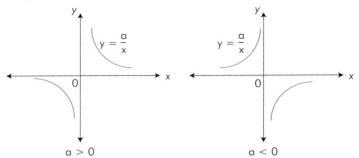

$a > 0$ $a < 0$

In this course, students are expected to sketch curves by setting up a table of values, plotting the points and then using the basic graphs above to form the curve.

Example

Draw the graph of $y = x^2 - 4$
for $-3 \le x \le 3$.

Solution

Set up a table of values.

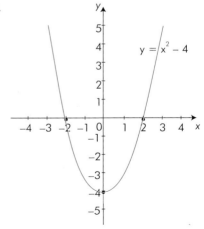

x	y
-3	5
-2	0
-1	-3
0	-4
1	-3
2	0
3	5

Algebraic substitution

This involves finding the value of an algebraic expression by substituting numerical values in place of the letters (pronumerals).

Example

If $x = 5$, $y = 3$ and $z = 20$ evaluate:

a $x + y + z$ **b** $8y - z$ **c** $\dfrac{z}{x} + xy$

Solution

a $x + y + z = 5 + 3 + 20 = 28$

b $8y - z = 8 \times y - z = 8 \times 3 - 20 = 24 - 20 = 4$

c $\dfrac{z}{x} + xy = \dfrac{20}{5} + 5 \times 3$ (**Note:** $\dfrac{20}{5} = 20 \div 5$)

             $= 4 + 15 = 19$

Simplifying algebraic expressions

An algebraic expression is a collection of algebraic terms, with their + and − signs.

Algebraic conventions

- In addition:
  $a + a + b + b + a = 3a + 2b$

- In subtraction:
  $3a - 2b - a - b = 2a - 3b$
  Note: You can only add and subtract like terms.

- In multiplication:
  $a \times b = ab$, $a \times a = a^2$
  $2 \times a \times b = 2ab$, $a \times a \times a = a^3$
  Note: When multiplying like terms, add the powers.

- In division:
  $a \div b$ is written as $\dfrac{a}{b}$ $a^2 \div a = a$, $a^2b^3 \div ab = ab^2$

Note: When dividing like terms, subtract the powers.

33

- Removing brackets

  Multiply the term outside the brackets by each term inside the brackets.

  Single brackets: $a(b \pm c) = ab \pm ac$
  $$-a(b \pm c) = -ab \mp ac$$

  Double brackets: $(a + b)(c + d) = a(c + d) + b(c + d)$
  $$= ac + ad + bc + bd$$

Example

Simplify the following.

a $2x - 4y + 5x + y$

b $2a \times 2a \times 3a$

c $\dfrac{2xy}{3} \div \dfrac{x^2}{9}$

Solution

a $2x - 4y + 5x + y = 2x + 5x + y - 4y = 7x - 3y$

b $2a \times 2a \times 3a = 2 \times 2 \times 3 \times a \times a \times a = 12a^3$

c $\dfrac{2xy}{3} \div \dfrac{x^2}{9} = \dfrac{2xy \times 9}{3 \times x^2} = \dfrac{^3 9 \times 2 \times \cancel{x}^1 \times y}{_1 3 \times _1 \cancel{x} \times x} = \dfrac{6y}{x}$

Factorising

- $ab + bc = b(a + c)$
- $ac + ad + bc + bd = a(c + d) + b(c + d)$
  $$= (a + b)(c + d)$$

Example

Factorise $ax + 3a - 3bx - 9b$.

Solution

$ax + 3a - 3bx - 9b = a(x + 3) - 3b(x + 3)$
$$= (a - 3b)(x + 3)$$

Rearranging formulae

Rearranging a formula means changing the subject of the formula.

Example

Make x the subject of the following.

a $A = \dfrac{3x}{4y}$ **b** $x^2 + y^2 = 16$

Solution

a $A = \dfrac{3x}{4y} \Rightarrow 4Ay = 3x$ *Multiply both sides by 4y.*

$$\frac{4Ay}{3} = x \qquad \textit{Divide both sides by 3.}$$

$$x = \frac{4Ay}{3}$$

b $x^2 + y^2 = 16 \Rightarrow x^2 = 16 - y^2$ *Subtract y^2 from both sides.*

$$x = \pm\sqrt{16 - y^2} \quad \textit{Take the square root of both sides.}$$

Note: Don't forget both positive and negative roots.

Solving equations

To solve an equation, find the value of the unknown to make the equality true. The golden rule is: *Whatever operation (+, −, ×, ÷) is done to one side of the equation, must also be done to the other side.*

Example

Solve $5(x + 1) = x + 15$

Solution

$5(x + 1) = x + 15 \Rightarrow 5x + 5 = x + 15$ *Expand the brackets.*

$4x + 5 = 15$ *Subtract x from both sides.*

$4x = 10$ *Subtract 5 from both sides.*

$x = \dfrac{10}{4}$ *Divide both sides by 4.*

$x = 2\dfrac{1}{2}$ or 2.5

Problem-solving with equations

Many mathematical problems expressed in words can be translated into algebraic expressions and then solved.

Example

A year ago Eden was twice Amanda's age. If the sum of their current ages is 44, how old are Eden and Amanda now?

Solution

Let Amanda's age now = x, so that a year ago her age = $(x - 1)$.

Eden's age a year ago was twice that of Amanda's so was $2(x - 1)$.
∴ Eden's age now = $2(x - 1) + 1$.

$$\begin{aligned}
\text{Now} \quad x + 2(x - 1) + 1 &= 44 \\
x + 2x - 2 + 1 &= 44 \\
3x - 1 &= 44 \\
3x &= 45 \\
x &= 15
\end{aligned}$$

∴ Amanda's age now = 15 years and Eden's age = $44 - 15 = 29$.

Inequalities and graphs

An inequality is an expression in which one side is not equal to the other. You need to know the symbols that describe which is bigger.

> 'is greater than'	⩾ 'is greater than or equal to'
< 'is less than'	⩽ 'is less than or equal to'

Solving linear inequalities

In solving linear inequalities, remember that the inequality sign is:

- unchanged if you add or subtract the same positive or negative number to both sides
- unchanged if the inequality is multiplied or divided by a positive number
- reversed if the inequality is multiplied or divided by a negative number.

Example

Solve: **a** $2x - 1 \geqslant 3$ **b** $3(1 - x) > 7 - x$.

Solution

a $2x - 1 \geqslant 3$

$\quad\quad 2x \geqslant 4$ *Add 1 to both sides.*

$\quad\quad\ \ x \geqslant 2$ *Divide both sides by 2.*

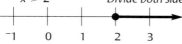

b $3(1 - x) > 7 - x$

$\quad 3 - 3x > 7 - x$ *Expand the brackets.*

$\quad\ \ \ ^-3x > 4 - x$ *Subtract 3 from both sides.*

$\quad\ \ \ ^-2x > 4$ *Add x to both sides.*

$\quad\quad\ \ x < ^-2$ *Divide both sides by $^-2$, note change of sign.*

Solving non-linear inequalities

Inequalities may also involve higher powers of x.

Example

Solve: $2x^2 - 8 > 0$.

Solution

$2x^2 - 8 > 0$

$\quad 2x^2 > 8$ *Add 8 to both sides.*

$\quad\ \ x^2 > 4$ *Divide both sides by 2.*

Since $-x \times -x = x^2$ and $x \times x = x^2$ you obtain two inequalities.

$\quad (x)^2 > 4$ and $(-x)^2 > 4$

$\quad\ \ x > 2$ and $-x > 2 \Rightarrow x < ^-2$

So $x > 2$ or $x < -2$.

Graphs of linear inequalities

Follow these steps when you need to draw graphs of linear inequalities.

Step 1: Replace the inequality sign by an equals (=) sign and draw the line or curve.
Use dotted lines if the inequality is 'less than' (<) or 'greater than' (>), and solid lines if the inequality is 'less than or equal to' (≤) or 'greater than or equal to' (≥).

Step 2: To find the required region, substitute a value not on the line.
If the inequality is satisfied then this is the required region and if it is not satisfied then the required region is on the other side of the line.

Step 3: Shade the area you do **not** want. Make it clear which is the required region.

Note: Always read the question carefully. Occasionally you may be asked to shade the required region.

Example

Find the region bound by the following inequalities.

$y \geq x - 1, x > {}^-1, y \leq 1$

Solution

Step 1: Sketch the lines for the graphs of
$y = x - 1, x = {}^-1, y = 1$
Note: The line $x = {}^-1$ is dotted.

Step 2: For $y \geq x - 1$ at $(0, 0)$, $0 \geq {}^-1$
∴ required region is to the LHS of the line.
For $x > {}^-1$ at $(0, 0)$, $0 > {}^-1$
∴ required region is to the RHS of the line.
For $y \leq 1$ at $(0, 0)$, $0 \leq 1$
∴ the required region is below the line.

Step 3: Shade the unwanted areas.

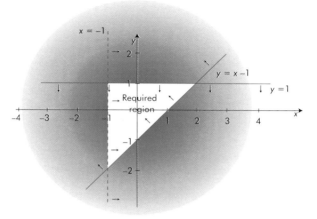

Simultaneous equations

Simultaneous equations are sets of equations that may be solved together, to find a set of values which make them all true simultaneously. You are usually asked to solve two equations. There are three methods.

- **Substitution method:** Make one of the unknowns the subject of one of the equations and then substitute it into the other equation.
- **Elimination method:** Make the coefficients of one of the unknowns the same in both equations, then add or subtract the two equations to eliminate one of the unknowns.
- **Graphical method:** Draw the graph of each function on the same set of axes; the **point of intersection** represents the solution.

Example

Solve the following simultaneous equations.

$3y - 2x = 12$
$4x - y = 1$

Solution

Method 1: Substitution method

$3y - 2x = 12$ 　　　　　　(1)
$4x - y = 1$ 　　　　　　(2)

Make y the subject of equation (2).

$y = 4x - 1$

Now substitute this into (1).

$3(4x - 1) - 2x = 12$
$12x - 3 - 2x = 12$
$10x - 3 = 12$
$10x = 15$
$x = \dfrac{15}{10}$
$= 1\dfrac{1}{2}$

Now, substituting $x = 1\dfrac{1}{2}$ into (2) gives:

$4(1\dfrac{1}{2}) - y = 1$
$6 - y = 1$
$y = 5$

The solution is $x = 1\dfrac{1}{2}$, $y = 5$.

Method 2: Elimination method

$3y - 2x = 12$ 　　　　　　(1)
$4x - y = 1$ 　　　　　　(2)

Multiply equation (1) by 2.

$$6y - 4x = 24 \qquad (3)$$

Now add.

(3) + (2) gives:

$$5y = 25$$
$$y = 5$$

Substituting $y = 5$ into (2) gives:

$$4x - 5 = 1$$
$$4x = 6$$
$$x = \frac{6}{4}$$
$$= 1\frac{1}{2}$$

The solution is $x = 1\frac{1}{2}$, $y = 5$.

Method 3: Graphical method

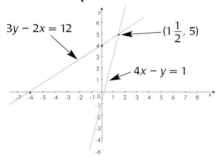

$3y - 2x = 12$

$(1\frac{1}{2}, 5)$

$4x - y = 1$

Since $3y - 2x = 12$ and $4x - y = 1$ intersect at $(1\frac{1}{2}, 5)$

The solution is $x = 1\frac{1}{2}$, $y = 5$.

Note: As you would expect, all three methods give the same solution.

Quadratics

Factorising quadratics

Here are some results that you will find it useful to know.

- $a^2 + 2ab + b^2 = (a + b)^2$
- $a^2 - 2ab + b^2 = (a - b)^2$
- $(a - b)(a + b) = a^2 - b^2$
- $x^2 + (a + b)x + ab = (x + a)(x + b)$

Example

Factorise $4x^2 - 9$.

Solution

$$4x^2 - 9 = (2x)^2 - (3)^2$$
$$= (2x - 3)(2x + 3)$$

Solving simple quadratics

You need to be able to solve simple quadratic equations by factorising first, then applying the following rule.

If $a \times b = 0$, then either $a = 0$, or $b = 0$ or both.

Example

Factorise, then solve for x.

a $x^2 - x - 2 = 0$ **b** $x^2 + 8x + 12 = 0$

Solution

a $x^2 - x - 2 = 0$
$(x - 2)(x + 1) = 0$
$\therefore (x - 2) = 0$ i.e. $x = 2$
or $(x + 1) = 0$ i.e. $x = -1$

Multiply to give x^2 $\left\{ \begin{matrix} x & -2 \\ x & +1 \end{matrix} \right\}$ Multiply to give -2

Middle term
$x - 2x = -x$

The solutions to the equation $x^2 - x - 2 = 0$ are $x = 2$ and $x = {}^-1$.

b $x^2 + 8x + 12 = 0$
$(x + 6)(x + 2) = 0$
$\Rightarrow (x + 6) = 0$ i.e. $x = {}^-6$
or $(x + 2) = 0$ i.e. $x = {}^-2$

$$\text{Multiply} \atop \text{to give} \atop x^2 \left\{ \begin{matrix} x & +6 \\ & \times \\ x & +2 \end{matrix} \right\} {\text{Multiply} \atop \text{to give} \atop 12}$$

The solutions to the equation
$x^2 + 8x + 12 = 0$ are $x = {}^-6$ and $x = {}^-2$.

Middle term
$6x + 2x = 8x$

Solving polynomials by trial and improvement

Trial and improvement can be used to provide successively better approximations to the solution of a polynomial equation.

Example

Solve $x^3 - 5x + 3 = 0$ correct to 1 decimal place, given that the solution lies in the range $1 \leqslant x \leqslant 2$.

Solution

When $x = 2$ $x^3 - 5x + 3 = 2^3 - 5 \times 2 + 3 = 1$
When $x = 1.5$ $x^3 - 5x + 3 = 1.5^3 - 5 \times 1.5 + 3$
                               $= -1.125$

So the solution lies between $x = 1.5$ and $x = 2$ (and seems to be closer to $x = 2$).

Try $x = 1.8$ $(1.8)^3 - 5(1.8) + 3 = {}^-0.168$

So the solution lies between $x = 1.8$ and $x = 2$ (and seems to be much closer to $x = 1.8$).

Try $x = 1.85$ $(1.85)^3 - 5(1.85) + 3 = 0.081\,625$

So the solution lies between $x = 1.8$ and $x = 1.85$.

i.e. $1.8 < x < 1.85$

Since any value in that range will be rounded to 1.8 (correct to 1 d.p.) the solution is $x = 1.8$ correct to 1 d.p.

Area under a graph – the trapezium rule

Trapezium rule

The area under a graph can be found by various methods, including counting squares. A better approximation is obtained by using the trapezium rule. First, divide the area into n strips, all of equal width.

Area $= \frac{1}{2}h[y_0 + 2(y_1 + y_2 + ... + y_{n-1}) + y_n]$

Area $= \frac{1}{2}h(\text{ends} + 2 \times \text{middle})$

where h is the width of the strip.

Area under a graph

The area under a graph can be expressed as:

units along the y-axis $\times$ units along the x-axis.

For example, the area under a speed–time graph represents the distance travelled (i.e. speed $\times$ time = distance).

Example

Use the trapezium rule to find an approximation to the area under the curve $y = 2^{x + 1}$ from $x = 1$ to $x = 4$.

Solution

Area $= \frac{1}{2}h(y_0 + 2(y_1 + y_2) + y_3)$

Area $= \frac{1}{2}(2^2 + 2(2^3 + 2^4) + 2^5)$ **Note:** $h = 1$

Area $= \frac{1}{2}(4 + 2 \times 24 + 32)$

     $= 42$ square units

Gradient and tangents

The gradient of a curve changes depending upon the point where you take it.

You can find the gradient of a curve at a point by drawing a tangent at that point and calculating its gradient.

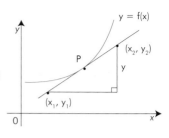

From the diagram the gradient of the curve at P is given by:

$$\text{gradient} = \frac{\text{change in } y}{\text{change in } x} = \frac{y_2 - y_1}{x_2 - x_1}$$

Travel graphs

This important application of gradients is a topic that is commonly tested in exams. The gradient of a distance-time travel represents **speed**. A flat (horizontal) section of line means that the object is stationary.

Further rearrangement of formulae

At the higher level you are required to rearrange formulae where the subject exists in more than one term.

Example

Make x the subject of $\dfrac{x - 1}{x + 1} = y$.

Solution

$$\frac{x - 1}{x + 1} = y$$

$(x - 1) = y(x + 1)$ *Multiply both sides by $(x + 1)$.*
$x - 1 = xy + y$ *Expand the brackets.*
$x - xy = 1 + y$ *Add $(1 - xy)$ to both sides.*
$x(1 - y) = 1 + y$ *Factorise.*
$x = \dfrac{1 + y}{1 - y}$ *Divide both sides by $(1 - y)$.*

45

Quadratic equations

At the higher level you will be expected to use various algebraic methods for solving more complicated quadratic equations.

Factorisation

Example

Solve for x: $3x^2 - 2x - 8 = 0$.

Solution

$3x^2 - 2x - 8 = 0$

$(3x + 4)(x - 2) = 0$

$\therefore (x - 2) = 0$ i.e. $x = 2$

or $(3x + 4) = 0$ i.e. $x = -\frac{4}{3}$

Multiply to give $3x^2$
$$\begin{Bmatrix} 3x & 4 \\ x & -2 \end{Bmatrix}$$
Multiply to give -8

Middle term
$4x - 6x = -2x$

The quadratic formula

The solution to the quadratic equation $ax^2 + bx + c = 0$ is given by:

$$x = \frac{-b \pm \sqrt{b^2 - 4ac}}{2a}$$

Note: Use the quadratic formula when the quadratic equation cannot be factorised easily, or when the question asks for solutions to be expressed to a number of decimal places.

Completing the square

An alternative method to those above (although not as popular) is completing the square. It involves converting quadratic equations into perfect squares.

Use the fact that $x^2 + 2bx = (x + b)^2 - b^2$.

Follow these steps to complete the square.

Step 1: Divide (if necessary) the quadratic equation by the coefficient of x^2, as the coefficient of x^2 must always be 1.

Step 2: Form the perfect square by halving the coefficient of x (i.e. b), adding b to x, and squaring (i.e. $(x + b)^2$).

Step 3: Subtract b^2 from the perfect square.

Example

Solve $2x^2 - 12x + 2 = 0$ by completing the square.

Solution

$2x^2 - 12x + 2 = 0$

Step 1: Divide throughout by 2 i.e. $x^2 - 6x + 1 = 0$.

Steps 2&3:
$$x^2 - 6x + 1 = 0$$
$$x^2 - 6x = {}^-1$$
$$(x - 3)^2 - ({}^-3)^2 = {}^-1$$
$$(x - 3)^2 - 9 = {}^-1$$
$$(x - 3)^2 = 8$$
$$x - 3 = \pm\sqrt{8}$$
$$x = 3 \pm 2\sqrt{2}$$ **Note:** $\sqrt{8} = 2\sqrt{2}$

Using graphs to solve equations

You can also solve equations by drawing the graph of each side of the equation. The point(s) of intersection give the solution(s).

Example

Use the graphs of $y = 4x^2$ and $y = 6 - 2x$ to solve $4x^2 = 6 - 2x$.

Solution

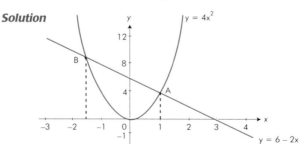

From the graph the points of intersection are A(1, 4) and B($^-$1.5, 9).

The solutions to $4x^2 = 6 - 2x$ are $x = 1$ and $x = {}^-1.5$.

47

Algebraic fractions

The principles involved in manipulating algebraic fractions are the same as those for arithmetic fractions.

Graphical transformations

You need to be familiar with the following graphical transformations to the basic curve $y = f(x)$.

- $y = f(x) + a$ shifts the curve a units **up** ($a > 0$) or a units **down** ($a < 0$).
- $y = f(x + b)$ shifts the curve b units **left** ($b > 0$) or b units **right** ($b < 0$).
- $y = {}^-f(x)$ **reflects** the curve in the **x-axis**.
- $y = f({}^-x)$ **reflects** the curve in the **y-axis**.
- $y = kf(x)$ has two possibilities:
  → for $k > 1$, the curve is **stretched up** by a factor k parallel to the y-axis
  → for $0 < k < 1$, the curve is **compressed down** by a factor k parallel to the y-axis.
- $y = f(kx)$ has two possibilities:
  → for $k > 1$, the curve is **compressed in** by a factor k parallel to the x-axis
  → for $0 < k < 1$, the curve is **stretched out** by a factor k parallel to the x-axis.

Example

Sketch the graph for $y_1 = x^2$ and then use it to sketch the following on the same set of axes.

$y_2 = (x - 2)^2$, $y_3 = x^2 - 4$, $y_4 = 4(x - 5)^2 - 2$, $y_5 = {}^-(x + 4)^2 + 2$

Solution

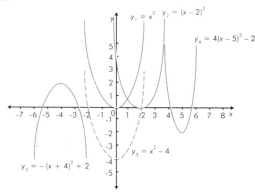

Notes: ● $y_2 = (x - 2)^2$ shifts y_1 2 units right ($b < 0$)
　　　　 ● $y_3 = x^2 - 4$ shifts y_1 4 units down ($a < 0$)
　　　　 ● $y_4 = 4(x - 5)^2 - 2$ has the following features when
　　　　　　compared to y_1:
　　　　　　stretched up as $k > 1$ ($k = 4$)
　　　　　　shifted 5 units to the **right** as $b < 0$
　　　　　　shifted 2 units **down** as $a < 0$.
　　　　 ● $y_5 = {}^-(x + 4)^2 + 2$ has the following features when
　　　　　　compared to y_1:
　　　　　　reflected in the x-axis
　　　　　　shifted 4 units to the **left** as $b > 0$
　　　　　　shifted 2 units **up** as $a > 0$.

Angles

Types of angles

1 **Acute angle**
   an angle that is less than 90°

2 **Obtuse angle**
   an angle that is greater than 90°
   but less than 180°

3 **Right angle**
   an angle of 90°

4 **Straight angle**
   an angle of 180°

5 **Reflex angle**
   an angle that is greater than 180°
   but less than 360°

6 **Revolution**
   an angle of 360°

7 **Complementary angles**
   two angles that add up to 90°

8 **Supplementary angles**
   two angles that add up to 180°

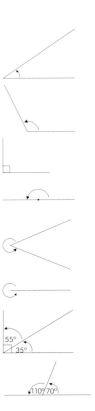

Three basic angle theorems

1 Angles in a straight line
Angles on a straight line sum to 180°.

$$x + y + z = 180$$

2 Angles at a point
Angles that meet at the same point sum to 360°.

$$a + b + c = 360$$

3 Vertically opposite angles
When two lines intersect, two pairs of vertically opposite angles are formed. Vertically opposite angles are equal.

$$w = y \text{ and } x = z$$

Parallel lines

When a pair of parallel lines cut a transversal, three different types of angles are formed.

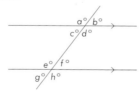

1 Corresponding angles
Corresponding angles (F angles) are equal.
$b = f, d = h, a = e, c = g$

2 Alternate angles
Alternate angles (Z angles) are equal.
$c = f, d = e$

3 Co-interior angles
Co-interior angles (C angles) are supplementary (sum to 180°).
$d + f = 180°, c + e = 180°$
Co-interior angles are also know as **allied** angles.

51

Triangles

Types of triangle

Name	Diagram	Properties
Acute-angled triangle		All angles are acute. (less than 90°)
Obtuse-angled triangle		One angle is obtuse. (more than 90°)
Right-angled triangle		One angle is a right angle. (90°)
Scalene triangle		All three sides are different lengths. All three angles are different.
Isosceles triangle		Two sides have equal lengths. Angles opposite the equal sides are equal.
Equilateral triangle		All three sides are equal in length. All three angles are equal. (60°)

Triangle properties

There are three important properties relating to triangles.

1 Angle sum of a triangle

The angle sum of
any triangle = 180°
$a + b + c = 180$

2 Isosceles triangle

The base angles of an
isosceles triangle are equal.
i.e. $\angle ABC = \angle ACB$,
also $AB = AC$.

3 Equilateral triangle

All angles of an
equilateral triangle are 60°.
$\angle BAC = \angle ACB = \angle ABC = 60°$

Also $AC = BC = AB$

Polygons

A polygon is a closed figure with three or more straight sides.

A polygon is named according to the number of sides it has.

No. of sides	Name	No. of sides	Name
3	Triangle	8	Octagon
4	Quadrilateral	9	Nonagon
5	Pentagon	10	Decagon
6	Hexagon	11	Undecagon
7	Heptagon	12	Dodecagon

A polygon is said to be **regular** if all its sides are equal in length
and all its angles are equal.

53

Angle properties

Sum of the exterior angles of any polygon = 360°.

$(a + b + c + d + e + f) = 360°$

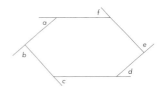

For a **regular polygon** with n sides:

- sum of exterior angles = 360°

  and each exterior angle = $\dfrac{360°}{n}$

- Sum of interior angles = $n(180° - \dfrac{360°}{n})$
  = $(n - 2)180°$

- Angle at the centre = $\dfrac{360°}{n}$

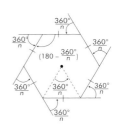

Quadrilaterals

Classification of quadrilaterals

Any closed four-sided polygon is called a quadrilateral.

Name	Shape	Properties
Trapezium		• One pair of opposite sides parallel
Parallelogram		• Opposite sides equal • Opposite sides parallel
Rhombus		• All sides equal • Opposite sides parallel
Rectangle		• Opposite sides equal • All angles 90°
Square		• All sides equal • All angles 90°

Quadrilateral property

The angle sum of any quadrilateral is 360°.
$a + b + c + d = 360$

Solids

A **solid** is a three-dimensional shape such as a cube, pyramid, cylinder, cone or sphere.

You need to know the following important terms.

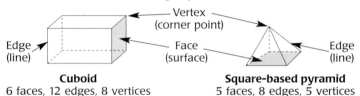

Cuboid
6 faces, 12 edges, 8 vertices

Square-based pyramid
5 faces, 8 edges, 5 vertices

Pyramids

A pyramid is named according to the shape of its base.

Name	Shape	Base
Square-based pyramid		Square
Rectangular-based pyramid		Rectangle
Triangular-based pyramid (tetrahedron)		Triangle

Prisms

A prism is a solid with a constant **cross-section**, which is parallel to the end faces and perpendicular to the length of the solid.

Name	Shape	Cross-section
Cuboid	cut	
Cube	cut	
Triangular prism	cut	
Pentagonal prism	cut	
Cylinder (circular prism)	cut	

Other solids

Name	Shape	Name	Shape
Sphere		Cone	
Cylinder		Hemisphere	

Nets of solids

The net of a solid is the 2D shape that can be folded to form the solid. When you draw a net, the length of each side must be the same as the corresponding length in the solid.

Congruent triangles

Two triangles are congruent if they are exactly the same shape and size (the three sides and angles of one triangle equal the three sides and angles of the other triangle).

The symbol ≡ means 'is congruent to'.

Four tests for congruent triangles

Two triangles are congruent if they satisfy any of the following four conditions.

- three corresponding pairs of equal sides **SSS**

- two corresponding sides and the included angle are equal **SAS**

- two corresponding angles and one corresponding side are equal **AAS**

- hypotenuse and one corresponding side equal, in a pair of right-angled triangles **RHS**

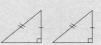

57

Similar triangles

Two triangles are similar if they have the same shape but are not the same size. Similar triangles satisfy any of these three tests.

- All corresponding angles are equal.

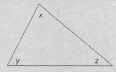

- All corresponding sides are in the same proportion.

$$\frac{a}{d} = \frac{b}{e} = \frac{c}{f}$$

- Two pairs of corresponding sides are in the same proportion and the included angle is the same.

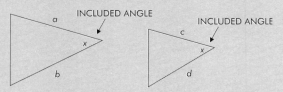

$\dfrac{a}{c} = \dfrac{b}{d}$ and the included angle is the same in both triangles.

The symbol ||| means 'is similar to'.

Using mathematical instruments

Constructing triangles

To construct a triangle you need to know:

- two angles and a side or
- two sides and the included angle or
- three sides.

Example

Construct a triangle ABC with sides of length 4.5 cm, 3.5 cm and 2.5 cm.

Solution

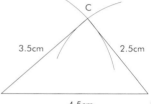

1 Draw the longest side AB.

2 Open your compasses to 3.5 cm and draw an arc from A.

3 Open your compasses to 2.5 cm and draw an arc from B.

4 Join the points A and B to the point where the arcs intersect to complete the triangle.

Geometrical constructions

You need to be able to carry out the following four constructions using only a ruler and a pair of compasses.

- **Perpendicular bisector of a line**

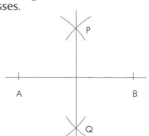

1 Draw a line AB.

2 Open your compasses to a radius greater than half the length of AB and draw arcs above and below the line from both A and B.

3 Join the points where the arcs intersect (P and Q) to form the perpendicular bisector of AB.

- **Perpendicular from a point X on a straight line**

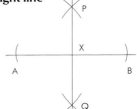

1 Open your compasses to about
   1.5 cm and draw arcs from X to
   cut the line at A and B.

2 Now construct the perpendicular
   bisector of the line segment AB
   as described earlier.

- **Perpendicular from point P to a straight line**

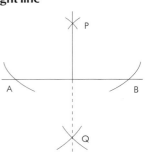

1 Open your compasses to a suitable
   radius and draw arcs from P to
   cut the line at A and B.

2 With your compasses set to the
   same radius as in 1, draw arcs on
   the opposite side of P from both
   A and B.

3 Joint the point where the arcs
   intersect (Q) with P to form the
   perpendicular from point P
   to the line.

- **The bisector of angle ABC**

1 Open your compasses to a radius of about 3 cm and draw arcs
   from B to cut BA and BC at L and M respectively.

2 With the compasses still set to the same radius, draw arcs from
   L and M between BA and BC.

3 Join the point where the arcs intersect (Q) with B to form the
   bisector of angle ABC.

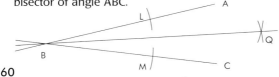

Symmetry

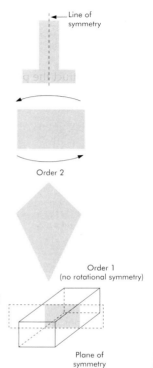

- **Reflective symmetry** occurs when half the 2D shape can be reflected in a mirror line (known as the **line of symmetry**) to form the whole shape.

- **Rotational symmetry** occurs when a 2D shape is rotated (turned) and it looks exactly the same.

  The **order** of rotational symmetry is the number of times a shape looks the same in a 360° turn. For example a regular hexagon has rotational symmetry of order 6.

  Rotational symmetry **of order of 1** means the shape has no rotational symmetry as it only looks the same when it has completed the 360° turn (i.e. returned to its initial position).

- A 3D shape has **plane symmetry** when it can be divided into two equal halves by a plane cutting the solid.

Pythagoras' theorem

Pythagoras' theorem states that:

> In any right-angled triangle, the square of the hypotenuse (the longest side) is equal to the sum of the squares of the other two sides.

$$c^2 = a^2 + b^2$$

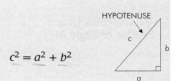

Trigonometric ratios

These ratios are vitally important and should be memorised.
They are based on any right-angled triangle.

$$\sin \theta = \frac{\text{opposite}}{\text{hypotenuse}} \quad \text{(SOH)}$$

$$\cos \theta = \frac{\text{adjacent}}{\text{hypotenuse}} \quad \text{(CAH)}$$

$$\tan \theta = \frac{\text{opposite}}{\text{adjacent}} \quad \text{(TOA)}$$

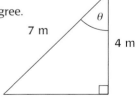

Hint: To help you remember the three ratios, here is a mnemonic.

S	**O**	**H**	**C**	**A**	**H**	**T**	**O**	**A**
h	n	e	r	f	e	r	v	l
a		n	y	t		i	e	i
m		r	i	e		p	r	c
e		y	n	r		p		e
			g			e		
						d		

Finding sides and angles

Trigonometric ratios can be used to find:

● the length of a side, given an angle and one side
● the size of an angle given two sides, in a right-angled triangle.

Example

Find the size of angle θ, to the nearest degree.

Solution

$$\cos \theta = \frac{\text{adjacent}}{\text{hypotenuse}} = \frac{4}{7}$$

$$\theta = \cos^{-1} \frac{4}{7} = 55.150\,095\,42° = 55°$$

Note: Use $\cos^{-1} \frac{4}{7}$ or (arccos $\frac{4}{7}$) to show that you are working backwards to find the angle.

62

Angles of elevation and depression

Angles of elevation and depression are always measured from the horizontal.

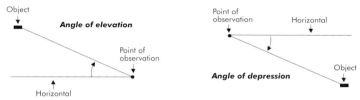

Example

From the top of a building 20 metres high, the angle of depression of a car on the street below is 25.5°. Find the distance of the car from the base of the building (to the nearest metre).

Solution

Let x be the horizontal distance
from the base of the building to the car.

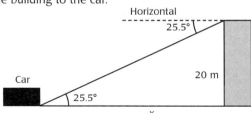

$\tan 25.5° = \dfrac{20}{x}$

$\therefore x = \dfrac{20}{\tan 25.5°}$

  $= 41.930\,871\,98$

  $= 42$ m to the nearest metre

$\therefore$ The car is 42 m away from the base of the building.

Tessellations

A tessellation is a pattern of 2D shapes that
fit together with no gaps.

The angles at each point in the pattern must add up to 360°.

Example

A floor is tessellated with equilateral
triangles and a regular polygon,
as shown.

Find the number of sides of the
regular polygon.

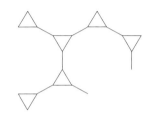

Solution

Taking one of the tessellations gives:

$$\frac{360° - 60°}{2} = \frac{300°}{2} = 150°$$

because angles that meet at a point add up to 360°.

∴ the interior angle of the polygon = 150°

Now, $150° = 180° - \dfrac{360°}{n}$ *Use the formula.*

$$\frac{360°}{n} = 30°$$

$$n = \frac{360°}{30°} = 12$$

∴ the regular polygon has 12 sides.

Note: A polygon with 12 sides is called an dodecagon.

64

Bearings

Bearings are always measured **clockwise** from **north**. They are expressed in the form $XXX°$ where $000° \leqslant XXX° \leqslant 360°$.

Diagram 1

Diagram 2

The bearing of A from O is 135°.   The bearing of A from O is 330°.

An alternative way of representing the angles shown in the diagrams above is to use standard compass bearings. This is expressed as a number of degrees (less than 90) east or west of north or south. For example:

- Diagram 1: S45°E
- Diagram 2: N30°W

Example

A ship sails due west from O for 40 km and then sails 25 km due south. Find the bearing of the ship from O to the nearest degree.

Solution

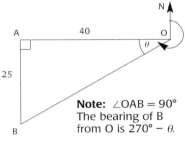

Let $\angle AOB = \theta$

Looking at $\triangle OAB$:
$$\tan \theta = \frac{AB}{OA} = \frac{25}{40} = 0.625$$

$\therefore \ \theta = 32°$ to the nearest degree

Now, the bearing of
B from O $= 270° - \theta$
$= 270° - 32°$
$= 238°$

Note: $\angle OAB = 90°$
The bearing of B
from O is $270° - \theta$.

$\therefore$ the bearing of the ship from O is 238°.

Transformations

A transformation alters the size or position of a shape. There are four types of transformations that you need to know about.

Translations

Translations shifts the position of a shape *a* units right or left and *b* units up or down, but its size remains the same. You can use **vector notation** to describe this movement:

$$\begin{pmatrix} a \\ b \end{pmatrix} \Rightarrow \left(\begin{array}{c} a \text{ units to the right } (a > 0) \text{ or } a \text{ units to the left } (a < 0) \\ b \text{ units up } (b > 0) \text{ or } b \text{ units down } (b < 0) \end{array} \right)$$

Example

Draw the image of triangle ABC after a translation of 5 squares right and 2 squares up.

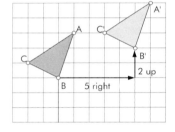

Solution

When the triangle is translated, each vertex is moved:
- 5 squares right and
- 2 squares up.

Mark the new positions of the vertices first, then join the points to form the image – the translated triangle.

Reflections

Reflections involve changing the position of an object by reflecting it in a mirror line. Again the size remains the same. The mirror line is known as the **axis of reflection**.

Example

Reflect triangle ABC in the mirror line shown.

Solution

Reflect each vertex of the triangle one at a time. The reflected vertex will be the same distance from the mirror line as the original vertex.

Join the vertices to form the new triangle – the image.

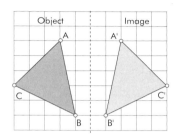

Compound reflections

You may be asked to carry out repeated reflections.

Example

a Reflect the figure ABCD shown below in the *y*-axis and call the image K.

b Reflect K in the line *y* = ⁻2 and call the image L.

Solution

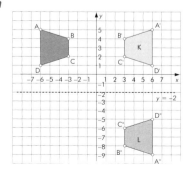

Example

Reflect the triangle ABC shown below in:

a the line $y = x$ and call the image P

b the line $y = {}^-x$ and call the image Q.

Solution

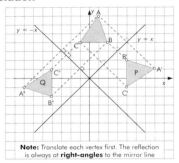

Note: Translate each vertex first. The reflection is always at **right-angles** to the mirror line

Rotations

In a rotation a figure is **turned** through an angle, about a fixed point called the **centre of rotation**. The shape of the figure remains the same.

To describe a rotation you must give:

- the **centre** of rotation
- the **direction** of rotation (clockwise or anticlockwise)
- the **angle** of rotation.

Example

Rotate the triangle ABC:
a 90° clockwise about O and call it P
b 90° anticlockwise about O and call it Q.

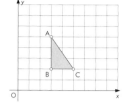

Solution

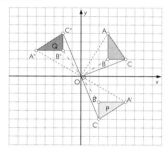

Rotate each vertex in turn, using these steps.

Step 1: Draw a line from the vertex to O and record its length.

Step 2: Use a protractor to measure 90° at O, in the required direction.

Step 3: Draw a line from O, along this angle, making it the same length as the line you drew in step 1.

Enlargements

Enlargements make a shape larger but do not change the basic shape of the object. The lengths in the object are multiplied by the **scale factor** to give the corresponding lengths in the image. The **centre of enlargement** is the point from which the enlargement takes place.

If the scale factor is greater than 1, the image is larger than the original object shape. Conversely, if the scale factor is less than 1, the image is smaller than the original object shape.

When the centre of enlargement is the origin, there is an easy method for performing the enlargement. Simply multiply the coordinates of the original figure by the scale factor to find the coordinates of the enlarged shape.

Example

Enlarge the triangle ABC by a scale factor of 2, centre of enlargement the origin (0, 0). Call the enlarged shape P.

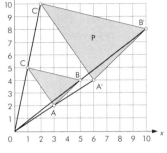

Solution

Let the vertices of the enlarged shape be A', B' and C'.

Now the coordinates of the given shape are:

A(3, 2), B(5, 4), C(1, 5).

The scale of enlargement is 2 and the centre of enlargement is the origin (0, 0), thus the coordinates of A', B' and C' are:

A'(6, 4), B'(10, 8), C'(2, 10).

Note: The enlargement could also have also been performed by noting that: OA' = 2OA, OB' = 2OB and OC' = 2OC.

Scale drawings

A scale drawing is usually an exact miniature representation of the original object.

The ratio of a scale drawing to the original is called the **scale**.

Scale = length in drawing : real length
e.g. a typical scale of a map is 1 cm : 1 km or 1 : 100 000.

Locus of points

A **locus** is the path followed by points that satisfy some given rule. You need to be familiar with the following loci (plural of locus).

Description of locus	Diagram
The locus of a point that moves so that it stays a fixed distance from a single fixed point is a **circle**.	Locus of points at a fixed distance from O
The locus of a point that moves so that it stays equidistant from two fixed points is the **perpendicular bisector** of the line joining the two points.	A • • B Locus of points at equal distance from A and B
The locus of a point that moves so that it is a fixed distance from a single fixed line is a **pair of parallel lines together with semicircles on either end.** **Note:** The ends of the line act like fixed points and so result in semicircles at each end.	P ⸺⸺⸺ Q Locus of points a fixed distance from line PQ
The locus of a point which moves such that it is equidistant from two intersecting lines is the **bisector of the angles between the lines.**	A locus D locus C B Locus of points equal distances from lines AB and CD
The locus of points that move so that the sum of its distances from two fixed points is constant is an **ellipse**.	Locus of points with constant combined distance from S and T PS + PT = QS + QT P S T Q

71

Example

Find the locus of points that are less than 1 cm from the outlines shown below.

Solution

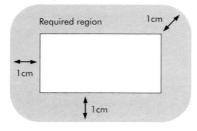

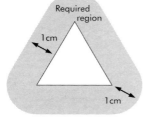

Perimeter

Name	Shape	Perimeter
Square		$4l$
Rectangle		$2l + 2b$
Circle		$2\pi r$ (or πd)

Area

Name	Shape	Area
Square		l^2 (length squared)
Rectangle		lb (length × breadth)
Triangle		$\frac{1}{2}bh$ ($\frac{1}{2}$ × base × height)
Parallelogram		bh (base × height)

73

Name	Shape	Area
Rhombus	y = length of diagonal x = length of diagonal	$\frac{1}{2}xy$ ($\frac{1}{2}$ product of diagonals)
Trapezium	a h b	$\frac{1}{2}h(a + b)$ ($\frac{1}{2}$ sum of parallel sides × height)

Volume

Name	Shape	Volume
Cube	l	l^3
Cuboid	h l b	lbh
Cylinder	r h	$\pi r^2 h$
Any prism	where h = height A = area of the cross-section	Ah

Note: The area of a trapezium and volume of a prism will be supplied in the exam paper at the Intermediate level.

Units for perimeter, area and volume

You should be able to identify the units for perimeter, area and volume by looking at the formulae.

- Perimeter is one-dimensional – it involves only the sum of lengths.
- Area is two-dimensional – it involves the product of two lengths (i.e. $(length)^2$).
- Volume is three-dimensional – it involves the product of three lengths (i.e. $(length)^3$).

Notes:

- The sum or difference of **like** units remains the same (e.g. the sum of two areas is still area).
- The sum or difference of **different** units is meaningless (e.g. the sum of volume and length is meaningless).

Example

In these formulae, you are given that a, b and c are all lengths. Identify the units for each formula.

a $2\sqrt{a^2 + bc}$

b $\dfrac{\pi(a^3 + 2abc)}{2\sqrt{2}}$

c $\dfrac{(a^2 - b^2)^2}{2abc}$

Solution

a $2\sqrt{a^2 + bc}$

$$= \text{number} \times \sqrt{\text{length}^2 + \text{length} \times \text{length}}$$

$$= \text{number} \times \sqrt{\text{length}^2 + \text{length}^2}$$

= number $\times \sqrt{\text{length}^2}$ *Sum of like units remains the same.*

= number $\times$ length $\sqrt{\text{length}^2} = \text{length}$

$\therefore$ the required units are length.

b $\dfrac{\pi(a^3 + 2abc)}{2\sqrt{2}}$

= number $\times$ (length^3 + number $\times$ length $\times$ length $\times$ length) $\div$ number

= $\dfrac{\text{number} \times (\text{length}^3 + \text{length}^3)}{\text{number}}$

= number $\times$ length^3 *Sum of like units remains the same.*

$\therefore$ the required units are length^3 i.e. volume.

c $\dfrac{(a^2 - b^2)^2}{2abc}$

= $\dfrac{(\text{length}^2 - \text{length}^2)^2}{\text{number} \times \text{length} \times \text{length} \times \text{length}}$

= $\dfrac{(\text{length}^2)^2}{\text{number} \times \text{length}^3}$

= $\dfrac{\text{length}^4}{\text{number} \times \text{length}^3} = \dfrac{\text{length}}{\text{number}}$

$\therefore$ the required units are length.

Further areas and volume

Surface areas

Name	Shape	Surface area
Cube		$6l^2$
Cuboid		$2(lb + lh + bh)$
Cylinder		$2\pi rh$ (hollow) $2\pi rh + \pi r^2$ (open one end) $2\pi rh + 2\pi r^2$ (closed)
Cone		πrl (open) $\pi rl + \pi r^2$ (closed)
Sphere		$4\pi r^2$

Volume

Name	Shape	Volume
Cone		$\frac{1}{3}\pi r^2 h$
Sphere		$\frac{4}{3}\pi r^3$
Cylinder		$\pi r^2 h$
Any pyramid where A = area of the base $\qquad h$ = perpendicular height		$\frac{1}{3}Ah$

Areas and volumes of similar figures

If the corresponding sides of two similar figures or solids are in the ratio $a : b$, then:

- the corresponding areas are in the ratio $a^2 : b^2$.

- the corresponding volumes are in the ratio $a^3 : b^3$.

Example

The volume of a cone of height 10 cm is 150 cm^3.
What is the volume of a similar cone of height 14 cm?

Solution

Ratio of lengths $= 10 : 14$ *Use the respective heights.*
                  $= 5 : 7$ *Cancel.*

Ratio of volumes $= 5^3 : 7^3$
                   $= 125 : 343$
                   $= 1 : 2.744$ *Divide both sides by 125.*

$\therefore$ Volume of cone of height 14 cm is $2.744 \times 150 = 411.6$ cm^3.

Three-dimensional trigonometry

At the higher level you will be required to deal with trigonometry in three dimensions. For these problems, it is often useful to draw a simple diagram to help you see which part of the solid you are working on.

Example

A right square pyramid has base ABCD and vertex V. Its perpendicular height h is half the length of the base AB. Find angle θ between the base edge AB and the sloping edge AV to the nearest degree.

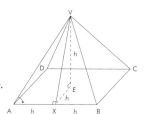

Solution

Consider triangle VEX:

$VX^2 = XE^2 + VE^2$ *By Pythagoras' theorem*

$VX^2 = h^2 + h^2 = 2h^2$

$VX = \sqrt{2}\,h$

Consider triangle AVX:

$\tan\theta = \dfrac{\sqrt{2}h}{h} = \sqrt{2}$

$\therefore\ \theta = \tan^{-1}\sqrt{2} = 55°$

Sin, cos and tan of any angle

Use the mnemonic **ASTC** – '**All Stations To Central**' to remember the sign of the functions sin, cos and tan for the four quadrants.

All ratios positive in the 1st quadrant.

Sin only positive in the 2nd quadrant.

Tan only positive in the 3rd quadrant.

Cos only positive in the 4th quadrant.

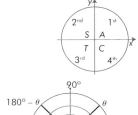

When you are solving trigonometric equations the 'criss-cross' angles are most relevant (shown as θ between the bold lines).

Noting that all angles are measured anticlockwise from the positive x-axis, the **positive solutions** for the various trigonometric identities are as follows:

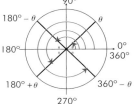

- for **sin** the solutions are θ and $180° - \theta$
- for **cos** the solutions are θ and $360° - \theta$
- for **tan** the solutions are θ and $180° + \theta$.

The **negative solutions** are as follows:

- for **sin** the solutions are $180° + \theta$, $360° - \theta$
- for **cos** the solutions are $180° - \theta$, $180° + \theta$
- for **tan** the solutions are $180° - \theta$, $360° - \theta$.

Example

Solve $\tan x = 0.5$ for $0 \leqslant x \leqslant 360°$.

Solution

$\tan x = 0.5 \Rightarrow x = \tan^{-1} 0.5 = 26.6°$ to 1 d.p.　　*'Criss-cross' angle*

Noting tan is positive in the 1st and 3rd quadrants:
$x = 26.6°, (180° + 26.6°) = 26.6°, 206.6°$

Sin, cos and tan graphs

To draw the graphs of these functions, use your calculator to set up a table of values. When you have drawn one period, you can repeat the curve.

- $y = \sin x$ Period $= 360°$, amplitude $= 1$

x	0°	90°	180°	270°	360°
$\sin x$	0	1	0	−1	0

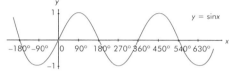

- $y = \cos x$ Period $= 360°$, amplitude $= 1$

x	0°	90°	180°	270°	360°
$\cos x$	1	0	−1	0	1

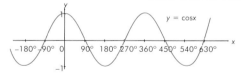

- $y = \tan x$ Period $= 180°$, amplitude is undefined

x	−90°	0°	90°	180°	270°
$\tan x$	undefined	0	undefined	0	undefined

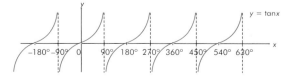

81

The sine and cosine rules

The sine rule

$$\frac{a}{\sin A} = \frac{b}{\sin B} = \frac{c}{\sin C}$$

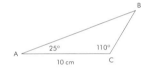

Use the sine rule to:

- find the length of a side where two angles and one side are given
- find the size of an angle where two sides and one angle opposite one of the two sides are given

where a, b and c are the sides opposite the angles A, B and C.

The alternative form is:

$$\frac{\sin A}{a} = \frac{\sin B}{b} = \frac{\sin C}{c}$$

Example

Find the length of BC correct to one decimal place.

Solution

$\angle ABC = 180° - 110° - 25° = 45°$

The sine rule gives:

$$\frac{a}{\sin A} = \frac{b}{\sin B}$$

$$\frac{BC}{\sin 25°} = \frac{10}{\sin 45°}$$

$$BC = \frac{10 \times \sin 25°}{\sin 45°}$$

$$= 5.976...$$

BC = 6 cm correct to one decimal place.

The cosine rule

$a^2 = b^2 + c^2 - 2bc\cos A$ or

$$\cos A = \frac{b^2 + c^2 - a^2}{2bc}$$

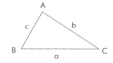

where b and c are two sides, A is the included angle and a is the remaining side. Use the cosine rule to:

- find the length of a side where two sides and the included angle are given
- find the size of an angle where all three sides are given.

The area of a triangle

To find the area of any triangle, use:

$$A = \frac{1}{2}ab\sin C$$

where a and b are two sides and
C is the included angle.

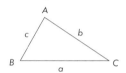

Arc, sector and segment

Parts of a circle

Part	Diagram
Arc The curve between two points on the circumference of the circle	![Arc diagram]
Sector A slice of the circle, cut off by two radii	![Sector diagram]
Segment A slice of the circle, cut off by a chord	![Segment diagram]

Arc length, area of a sector and area of a segment

Length of arc AB $= \dfrac{\theta}{360°} \times 2\pi r$ units

Area of sector OAB $= \dfrac{\theta}{360°} \times \pi r^2$ units^2

Area of segment = area of sector OAB − area of △OAB

$$= \dfrac{\theta}{360°} \times \pi r^2 - \dfrac{1}{2}r^2 \sin \theta \text{ units}^2$$

Circle geometry

This diagram shows the main parts of a circle
and the names given to them.

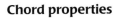

Chord properties

1 The perpendicular from the centre of the
   circle to the chord bisects the chord and,
   conversely, the line joining the centre of
   the circle to the midpoint of a chord is
   perpendicular to the chord.   AM = MB

2 Chords in a circle that are equidistant
   from the centre are equal in length and,
   conversely, equal chords in a circle
   (or in equal circles) are equal distances   AB = CD
   from the centre.   OM = ON

Angle properties

3 The angle subtended at the centre is
   twice the angle subtended by the same
   arc at the circumference.

4 Angles subtended at the circumference
   by the same arc are equal.

$$\angle ACB = \angle ADB$$
$$\angle CBD = \angle CAD$$

5 The angle in a semicircle is a right angle.

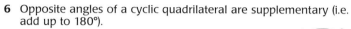

Cyclic quadrilaterals

A **cyclic** quadrilateral has all four vertices lying on the circumference of a circle.

Concyclic points are points through which a circle can be drawn (i.e. all points lie on the circumference of the circle).

6 Opposite angles of a cyclic quadrilateral are supplementary (i.e. add up to 180°).

7 If the opposite angles of a quadrilateral are supplementary, the quadrilateral is cyclic (also a test for four points to be concyclic).

$$x + y = 180°$$
$$w + z = 180°$$

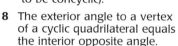

8 The exterior angle to a vertex of a cyclic quadrilateral equals the interior opposite angle.

$$\angle ABC = \angle ADE$$
$$\angle BCF = \angle BAD$$

Tangent properties

A **tangent** is a straight line that touches a circle at one point only.

9 The tangent is perpendicular to the radius through the point of contact.

10 Two tangents drawn to a circle from an external point are equal in length.

11 A line joining the centre of a circle to a point outside the circle:

  ● bisects the angle between the two tangents to the circle from that point

  ● bisects the angle between the radii drawn perpendicular to the tangents.

12 The angle between a tangent and a chord is
equal to the angle in the alternate segment.

Note: This is a very important theorem and is
often tested in exams. $\angle BAT = \angle BTD$

$\angle ABT = \angle ATE$

Enlargement by a negative scale factor

At the Higher level you are required to enlarge figures by a
negative scale factor. This means that the enlargement is situated
on the opposite side of the centre of enlargement.

Example

Enlarge the figure ABCD by a factor of $-\frac{1}{2}$ about (0, 1).

Solution

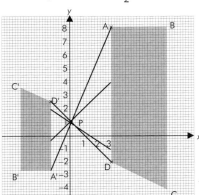

Notes:

- Corresponding lengths on A'B'C'D' are half those on ABCD.
- The image (enlargement) is on the opposite side of the centre (0, 1).
- $PA' = \frac{1}{2}PA$, $PB' = \frac{1}{2}PB$, $PC' = \frac{1}{2}PC$ and $PD' = \frac{1}{2}PD$.

Vectors

Vector notation

A **vector** quantity has **magnitude** (i.e. size) and **direction**. Vector quantities include velocity and displacement.

The vector from A to B is denoted by $\overrightarrow{AB}$.

Vectors may also be denoted by single letters printed in **bold** face (e.g. **a**, **b**, **c**).

Operations with vectors

- **Equal vectors**

Vectors are equal if they have the same **magnitude** and **direction**.

- **The addition of vectors**

The triangle law

The diagram shows three vectors $\overrightarrow{AB}$, $\overrightarrow{BC}$ and $\overrightarrow{AC}$ such that $\overrightarrow{AC} = \overrightarrow{AB} + \overrightarrow{BC}$.
Vector $\overrightarrow{AC}$ is the **resultant**.

Explanation: Suppose you walked from A to B ($\overrightarrow{AB}$) then from B to C ($\overrightarrow{BC}$), following the arrows. At point C your position relative to the starting point is given by $\overrightarrow{AC}$. Thus $\overrightarrow{AB} + \overrightarrow{BC} = \overrightarrow{AC}$.

Note: The vectors $\overrightarrow{AB}$ and $\overrightarrow{BC}$ follow on from each other, then $\overrightarrow{AC}$ joins the tail of vector $\overrightarrow{AB}$ to the head of vector $\overrightarrow{BC}$. The sum of the two vectors has A as its tail and C as its head, i.e. $\overrightarrow{AB} + \overrightarrow{BC} = \overrightarrow{AC}$. This is the **triangle law**.

The parallelogram law

This is the second law concerning the addition of vectors. The **parallelogram law** states that going from A to C via D is the same as going from A to C via B.

$\overrightarrow{AB} + \overrightarrow{BC} = \overrightarrow{AC}$ also $\overrightarrow{AD} + \overrightarrow{DC} = \overrightarrow{AC}$

i.e. $\overrightarrow{AB} + \overrightarrow{BC} = \overrightarrow{BC} + \overrightarrow{AB}$

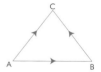

● The negative of a vector

The negative of a vector $\vec{AB}$ is a vector
equal in length but opposite in direction.

$^-\vec{AB} = \vec{BA}$

$\vec{AB}$

A ———————→ B

A ←——————— B

$\vec{BA}$

● Subtraction of vectors

Given two vectors, $\vec{AB}$ and $\vec{AC}$, as shown
in the diagram, their difference can be found
as follows.

$$\vec{AB} - \vec{AC} = \vec{AB} + -(\vec{AC})$$
$$= \vec{AB} + \vec{CA}$$
$$= \vec{CA} + \vec{AB} \qquad \textit{Parallelogram law}$$
$$= \vec{CB} \qquad \textit{Triangle law}$$

Diagrammatically this can be represented as follows.

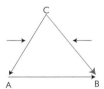

As $^-\vec{AC}$ has the
opposite direction
to $\vec{AC}$, reverse
the arrow.

Resultant vector in
moving from C to B.
$\vec{CB} = ^-\vec{AC} + \vec{AB}$
$\quad = \vec{AB} - \vec{AC}$

● Scalar multiplication

You do not need to be able to multiply vectors in the GCSE course
but you should be able to multiply them by a constant.

For a given vector **a** as shown:

- 2**a** is parallel to **a**, acts in the same direction
  but is twice as long

- $^-$3**a** is parallel to **a**, acts in the opposite
  direction and is three times as long.

Example

Vectors **u** and **w** are represented by the sides of triangle ABC as shown, and P is the midpoint of BC. Express **v** in terms of **u** and **w**.

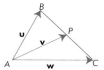

Solution

From the diagram:

$$\mathbf{v} = \vec{AP} = \vec{AB} + \vec{BP}$$

$$= \mathbf{u} + \tfrac{1}{2}BC \qquad \textit{P is the midpoint of BC.}$$

$$= \mathbf{u} + \tfrac{1}{2}(\mathbf{w} - \mathbf{u})$$

$$= \tfrac{1}{2}\mathbf{u} + \tfrac{1}{2}\mathbf{w}$$

Column vectors

The components of a vector are usually described in terms of:

- the number of units moved in the x-direction
- the number of units moved in the y-direction.

$$\text{vector} = \begin{pmatrix} x \\ y \end{pmatrix}$$

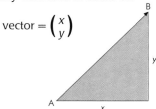

These units are best expressed as a **column vector**.

$$\begin{pmatrix} \text{change in } x\text{-value} \\ \text{change in } y\text{-value} \end{pmatrix}$$

To add or subtract column vectors, you simply add or subtract each component.

$$\begin{pmatrix} a \\ b \end{pmatrix} + \begin{pmatrix} c \\ d \end{pmatrix} = \begin{pmatrix} a + c \\ b + d \end{pmatrix}$$

To multiply a column vector by a constant you simply multiply each component.

$$k\begin{pmatrix} a \\ b \end{pmatrix} = \begin{pmatrix} ka \\ kb \end{pmatrix}$$

Example

Given $\mathbf{m} = \begin{pmatrix} 1 \\ -1 \end{pmatrix}$ and $\mathbf{n} = \begin{pmatrix} 2 \\ 1 \end{pmatrix}$ find $2\mathbf{n} - 3\mathbf{m}$.

Solution

$$2\mathbf{n} - 3\mathbf{m} = 2 \times \begin{pmatrix} 2 \\ 1 \end{pmatrix} - 3 \times \begin{pmatrix} 1 \\ -1 \end{pmatrix} = \begin{pmatrix} 4 \\ 2 \end{pmatrix} - \begin{pmatrix} 3 \\ -3 \end{pmatrix} = \begin{pmatrix} 1 \\ 5 \end{pmatrix}$$

Vectors in geometry

Vectors can be used to prove certain geometrical results.

Example

In the triangle ABC, X and Y are the midpoints of AB and AC respectively.

Given $\vec{XA} = \mathbf{a}$ and $\vec{AY} = \mathbf{b}$, show that BC = 2XY and BC is parallel to XY.

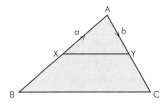

Solution

From the diagram:

$\vec{XY} = \mathbf{a} + \mathbf{b}$ *Triangle law of addition*

$\vec{BA} = \vec{BX} + \vec{XA}$ *As X is the midpoint of AB*

$\quad = \mathbf{a} + \mathbf{a} = 2\mathbf{a}$

$\vec{AC} = \vec{AY} + \vec{YC}$ *As Y is the midpoint of AC*

$\quad = \mathbf{b} + \mathbf{b} = 2\mathbf{b}$

Now $\vec{BC} = \vec{BA} + \vec{AC}$

$\quad\quad = 2\mathbf{a} + 2\mathbf{b}$

$\quad\quad = 2(\mathbf{a} + \mathbf{b})$

$\quad\quad = 2\vec{XY}$ *As $\mathbf{a} + \mathbf{b} = \vec{XY}$*

This shows that the magnitude of BC is twice the magnitude of XY so BC = 2XY. Since BC is a multiple of XY, then $\vec{BC}$ and $\vec{XY}$ are in the same direction and BC and XY are therefore parallel lines.

Numerical data

There are two types of numerical data:

- **discrete data** – each category is separate. This often takes whole number values, such as the number of students with blue eyes, or the make of car.

- **continuous data** – can include any value in a certain range that can be obtained by measurements, such as height of plants.

Gathered data

Data gathered as a result of a statistical investigation, such as a census or survey, is **primary** data. **Secondary** data is data that already exists. The three main methods of gathering data include:

- **observation** – gathering information and recording it on observation sheets, tape recorders or video recorders. It may be **systematic** (observer tries to be unobtrusive) or **participant** (observer participates in the activity).

- **interviewing** – personally asking questions of individuals or groups, using a **formal** (questions follow a definite format) or **informal** (questions follow a general format) approach.

- **questionnaires** – the most popular approach for gathering data, in which respondents complete the questionnaire in their own time.

When designing questionnaires, observe the following points.

- Identify clearly the **hypothesis** to be tested.

- Quote the length of time needed to complete the questionnaire and do not exceed it.

- Keep the questionnaire **clear and simple**.

- Do not seek extra information that is irrelevant to the hypothesis.

- Do not ask 'loaded' questions (trying to lead the respondent to a particular answer). All questions must be **unbiased**.

- Never give your opinion.

Collecting information

Collected data can be sorted into a **frequency table** or **tally chart**. For each observation, a tally (vertical line) is placed in the table. Every fifth tally is drawn through the previous four. The tallies are counted to find the frequency of each item (how often it occurs).

Grouping data

Discrete data

If the data covers a wide range of values it is customary to group the data into **class intervals** (i.e. a range of values). The class intervals have to be the same width.

Continuous data

For continuous data it is best to group the results into class intervals. The class intervals are often written using inequalities.

Example

The heights of 30 students were measured and recorded in a frequency table as shown.

Note: The class interval $140 \leqslant h < 150$ means the height is greater than or equal to 140 cm but less than 150 cm. A measurement of

Height (h cm)	Frequency
$130 \leqslant h < 140$	3
$140 \leqslant h < 150$	10
$150 \leqslant h < 160$	15
$160 \leqslant h < 170$	2
	Total = 30

150 cm would be included in the next class interval.

Displaying data

Data can be displayed in a number of different ways.

Bar charts

Bar charts use vertical bars or columns of equal width, with narrow spaces between them, to represent data.

Example

A survey was conducted to find the number of matches in each of 12 boxes. The results are shown on the bar chart.

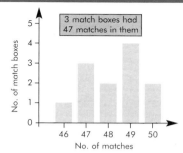

3 match boxes had 47 matches in them

Pie charts

Pie charts are circles cut up into different size sectors to represent the data. To calculate the angles for a pie chart, follow these steps.

Step 1: Find the total of the frequency column.

Step 2: Find the fraction that each item represents of the total found in step 1.

Step 3: Multiply the fraction in step 2 by 360° to find the angle for each item.

Example

The pie chart below shows the means of transport used by students to get to school.

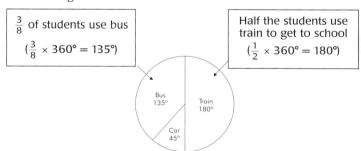

$\frac{3}{8}$ of students use bus

$(\frac{3}{8} \times 360° = 135°)$

Half the students use train to get to school

$(\frac{1}{2} \times 360° = 180°)$

93

Pictograms

In pictograms data is represented by identical symbols, equally spaced. Each symbol represents a certain number of items.

Example

The graph shows the number of students in Years 7–10 of a particular school.

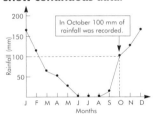

YEAR 7	𝄪𝄪𝄪𝄪𝄪𝄪𝄪
YEAR 8	𝄪𝄪𝄪𝄪𝄪𝄪
YEAR 9	𝄪𝄪𝄪𝄪
YEAR 10	𝄪𝄪𝄪𝄪
	𝄪 = 20 STUDENTS

Line graphs

Line graphs show how one variable changes relative to another. If you read the value on one axis, you can determine the value on the other axis. **Line graphs are used to show continuous data.**

Example

The rainfall in a particular town is graphed over a period of a year.

Frequency polygons

Set up a frequency distribution table and then draw the bar chart (or histogram) and its associated frequency polygon. Join up the midpoints of the bars to form the frequency polygon.

Example

Twenty students were each given a coin and asked to toss it four times and record the number of heads attained. Here are the results.

```
2    3    1    2    2    2    4    2    3    1
3    1    2    3    1    0    1    2    4    2
```

a Construct a frequency distribution table.

b Construct a bar chart and its associated frequency polygon.

94

Solution

a

Value (*x*)	Tally	Frequency (*f*)
0	I	1
1	IIII	5
2	IIII III	8
3	IIII	4
4	II	2

b

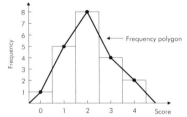

← Frequency polygon

Scatter diagrams and lines of best fit

Scatter diagrams show how two sets of data are related. This relationship is known as **correlation**. Correlation may be:

- **positive:** when the two variables increase with each other

- **negative:** when one variable increases as the other decreases

- **zero:** when there is no correlation between the variables.

In many practical situations, the points do not lie on a perfectly straight line. However, they may lie reasonably close to a straight line, so you can draw a **line of best fit** 'by eye', and use it to make predictions. To draw a scatter diagram follow these steps.

Step 1: Look at the data carefully, then choose suitable horizontal and vertical scales.

Step 2: Plot each point accurately, using a small, neat cross.

Step 3: Draw the line of best fit with roughly the same number of points above and below the line.

Measures of central tendency

Statistical notation

x = value	Σ = sum of
f = frequency	Σf = sum of frequency column
cf = cumulative frequency	xf = value × (frequency)
$\bar{x}$ = mean	Σxf = sum of xf column

Mode, median and mean

- Mode = most common value or, for a **group frequency distribution**, most common group (**modal** group).

- Mean = $\dfrac{\text{sum of all values}}{\text{number of values}} = \dfrac{\Sigma x}{n}$

  For a **frequency distribution** the mean is given by:

  mean = $\dfrac{\text{sum of (value × frequency)}}{\text{number of values}} = \dfrac{\Sigma xf}{\Sigma f}$

  For a group frequency distribution the mean is given by:

  mean = $\dfrac{\text{sum of (mid-interval value × frequency)}}{\Sigma f}$

- Median = middle vale when values are arranged in order of size

  → If the number of values (n) is odd, then the median is the $\left(\dfrac{n+1}{2}\right)$th value.

  → If the number of values (n) is even, then the median is the average of the $\left(\dfrac{n}{2}\right)$th and $\left(\dfrac{n+2}{2}\right)$th values.

To find the median of a **frequency distribution** you need first to form the cumulative frequency column and identify the middle value.

To find the median of a **group frequency distribution** you need to draw up a cumulative frequency diagram as shown later in this chapter.

Example

For the example on page 94 form a cumulative frequency distribution table and hence find the mode, median and mode.

Solution

Score (x)	Tally	Frequency (f)	Cumulative frequency (cf)	xf
0	|	1	1	0
1	||||	5	6	5
2	|||| |||	8	14	16
3	||||	4	18	12
4	||	2	20	8
		2		41

The mode is the value that occurs most often. In this case it is 2 (eight observations).

The median is the middle value.

Since there are 20 values, the median is the average of the:

$\frac{n}{2}$ th $= \frac{20}{2}$ th $=$ 10th and $\frac{n+2}{2}$ th $= \frac{22}{2}$ th $=$ 11th values.

$\therefore$ median $= \frac{2+2}{2} = 2$

Mean $= \frac{\Sigma xf}{\Sigma f} = \frac{41}{20} = 2.05$

Measures of spread

We use the **range** and the **interquartile range** to measure how spread out the data are.

Range

The range is the difference between the highest and lowest scores.

range = highest score − lowest score

The range does not provide a lot of information about the spread, as it depends only on the extreme values.

Interquartile range

The **interquartile range** is the difference between the upper quartile (Q_3) and the lower quartile (Q_1).

$IQR = Q_3 - Q_1$

Note: If there are n values in the distribution:

- the position of the upper quartile position is given by $\frac{3}{4}(n + 1)$

- the position of the lower quartile position is given by $\frac{1}{4}(n + 1)$.

Cumulative frequency diagrams

You can use cumulative frequency diagrams to find the median and the quartiles for a set of grouped data.

To draw a cumulative frequency diagram:

- plot the cumulative frequency against the **upper class boundary** for each class interval

- the cumulative frequency always goes on the vertical axis.

Example

The following information shows the waiting time (to the nearest minute) by patients at a local doctor's surgery.

Waiting time (minutes)	Frequency
1–5	2
6–10	6
11–15	16
16–20	28
21–25	12
26–30	3

Draw the cumulative frequency diagram for the information, then find:

a how many patients waited more than 12 minutes

b how many patients waited less than 24 minutes

c the median and the interquartile range.

Solution

First we need to work out the cumulative frequency and the upper boundary for each class interval.

Waiting time (minutes)	Upper boundary	Frequency (f)	Cumulative frequency (cf)
1–5	5.5	2	2
6–10	10.5	6	8
11–15	15.5	16	24
16–20	20.5	28	52
21–25	25.5	12	64
26–30	30.5	3	67

Note: The interval 1–5 will actually include times from 0.5 minutes to 5.5 minutes. Thus the upper boundary is 5.5.

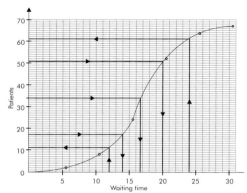

Note: The points plotted are the upper boundary against the cumulative frequency.

a From the graph, 11 patients waited less than 12 minutes so the number of patients who waited more than 12 minutes is $67 - 11 = 56$.

b From the graph, 61 patients waited less than 24 minutes.

c The median position is given by
$\frac{n + 1}{2} = \frac{67 + 1}{2} = 34$th value.

From the graph, the median = 16.75 minutes.

The interquartile range (IQR) = $Q_3 - Q_1$

The position of Q_3 is given by:
$\frac{3}{4}(n + 1) = \frac{3}{4}(67 + 1) = 51$st value.

The position of Q1 is given by

$\frac{1}{4}(n + 1) = \frac{1}{4}(67 + 1) = 17$th value.

From the graph, $Q_3 = 20.1$, $Q_1 = 14$.

∴ IQR $= 20.1 - 14 = 6.1$

The probability of an outcome

The probability of an outcome of an event can be defined as the chance of an outcome occurring.

Thus in an event or trial with n equally likely outcomes, the probability that a particular outcome A occurs is given by:

$$P(A) = \frac{\text{the number of ways } A \text{ can occur}}{\text{total number of outcomes } (n)}$$

Note: All probabilities must lie between 0 and 1 (i.e. $0 \leqslant P(A) \leqslant 1$).

The total of the probabilities of all the possible outcomes is 1.

The probability that an outcome does not occur

An outcome can either occur or not occur.

If $P(A)$ is the probability that A occurs and $P(A')$ is the probability that it does not occur, then:

$$P(A') = 1 - P(A)$$

Expected number

The expected number of successes in n trials is given by:

probability of success × number of trials

Example

If you throw a die 120 times, how many sixes would you expect to score?

Solution

Probability of success = probability of 6 = $\frac{1}{6}$

i.e. a 6 is expected $\frac{1}{6}$ of the time.

$\therefore$ expected number of sixes in 120 throws = $\frac{1}{6} \times 120 = 20$.

Relative frequency

The relative frequency that an outcome will happen is given by:

$$\text{relative frequency of an outcome} = \frac{\text{number of times the outcome occurred}}{\text{total number of trials}}$$

Relative frequency is used to estimate the actual probability. As the number of trials increases, the relative frequency gets closer to the expected probability.

Sample spaces

A sample space is a diagram that can be used to show the outcomes of various events. Tables are generally used for these.

Example

Brett throws two dice. Find the probability that the sum on the uppermost faces is:

a greater than 8   **b** less than 5.

Solution

Draw up a table of all possible outcomes:

		Second die					
		1	2	3	4	5	6
	1	**2**	**3**	**4**	5	6	7
	2	**3**	**4**	5	6	7	8
First	3	**4**	5	6	7	8	9*
die	4	5	6	7	8	9*	10*
	5	6	7	8	9*	10*	11*
	6	7	8	9*	10*	11*	12*

a P(greater than 8) $= \frac{10}{36} = \frac{5}{18}$ (indicated by *)

b P(less than 5) $= \frac{6}{36} = \frac{1}{6}$ (indicated in **bold**)

Mutually exclusive events

A and *B* are **mutually exclusive** if they cannot both happen at the same time.

If *A* and *B* are mutually exclusive, then:

P(*A* and *B*) = 0

MUTUALLY EXCLUSIVE

The additional rule of probability

Before applying the addition rule of probability, you must first identify whether the events are **mutually exclusive**.

A and *B* are **not** mutually exclusive events if they have some outcomes in common.

If *A* and *B* **are** mutually exclusive then:

P(*A* and *B*) = P(*A*) + P(*B*)

If *A* and *B* are **not** mutually exclusive then:

P(*A* or *B*) = P(*A*) + P(*B*) − P(*A* and *B*)

MUTUALLY EXCLUSIVE

NOT MUTUALLY EXCLUSIVE

Independent events

A and *B* are described as **independent events** if the probability of either event occurring is not affected by whether the other event has already occurred.

The multiplication rule of probability

If *A* and *B* are independent events, then:

P(*A* and *B*) = P(*A*) × P(*B*)

103

Tree diagrams

A tree diagram is a useful technique for representing the probabilities of combined events. It is also helpful in identifying the sample space.

The following rules apply to tree diagrams.

- **Multiply along the branches** to determine the probability of each outcome.
- If more than one path satisfies the conditions of a problem, add these probabilities.
- Probabilities along all the branches **sum to 1**.

Example

A factory produces batteries of which 2% are faulty. Using a tree diagram, find the probability that if two batteries are chosen only one is defective.

Solution

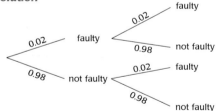

P(only one defective)
= P(faulty) × P(not faculty) + P(not faulty) × P(faulty)
= 0.02 × 0.98 + 0.98 × 0.02
= 0.0392

Sampling

A **population** is the whole set of items from which a sample can be drawn. A **sample** is only a portion of a population. You should be familiar with the following sampling techniques:

- **convenience sampling** − choose the first people who come along

- **random sampling** − choose a sample in which all items are equally likely to be chosen

- **systematic sampling** − involves random sampling: use some system to select the items of the population to be sampled

- **stratified sampling** − choose a sample that is representative of the population being considered, for example, if the population to be surveyed has twice as many men as women, the sample should also contain twice as many men as women

- **quota sampling** − involves choosing a sample with specific characteristics beforehand (e.g. office workers, children over 12).

Histograms − unequal class intervals

At the Higher level you need to be able to draw histograms in which the class intervals are not all equal. Follow these guidelines.

- The width of each column should be drawn to scale, on the horizontal axis, for the size of the class interval it represents. Columns may have different widths.

- The quantity on the vertical axis is the **frequency density** which is also the height of the column.

$$\text{frequency density (height)} = \frac{\text{frequency}}{\text{class width}}$$

- The area of each column represents the frequency for that class interval.

$$\text{class width} \times \text{column height} = \text{frequency}$$

You can draw the associated frequency polygon for a histogram by joining the midpoints of the tops of the columns.

Standard deviation

The standard deviation is a measure of how spread out the data are. It is a better measure of spread than the range or interquartile range as it takes account of all values of a distribution. A large standard deviation means the scores are widely spread, while a smaller standard deviation means that the scores are closer to the mean.

Standard deviation, s, for a set of numbers x_1, x_2, x_3, ..., x_n with a mean $\bar{x}$ is given by:

$$s = \sqrt{\frac{\sum(x - \bar{x})^2}{n}} \quad \text{or} \quad s = \sqrt{\frac{\sum x^2}{n} - \left(\frac{\sum x}{n}\right)^2}$$

Notes: • these formulae are provided on the examination paper

• variance $= s^2 = \dfrac{\sum(x - \bar{x})^2}{n}$

• the second formula is often easier to work with.

In a normal distribution:

• 68% of all data are within 1 standard deviation from the mean
• 95% of all data are within 2 standard deviations from the mean
• 99.7% of all data are within 3 standard deviations from the mean.

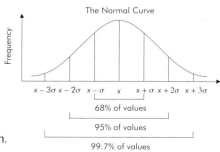

The Normal Curve

Note: The symbol σ means standard deviation.

Example

Find the standard deviation of the following scores.

56, 64, 41, 74, 90, 36, 50, 80, 45, 78.

Solution

Set up a table as follows.

x	56	64	41	74	90	36	50	80	45	78	$\Sigma x =$	614
x^2	3136	4096	1681	5476	8100	1296	2500	6400	2025	6084	$\Sigma x^2 =$	40794

Mean $= \dfrac{\Sigma x}{n} = \dfrac{614}{10} = 61.4$

Standard deviation $= \sqrt{\dfrac{\sum x^2}{n} - \left(\dfrac{\sum x}{n}\right)^2}$

$$= \sqrt{\dfrac{40\,794}{10} - \left(61.4\right)^2}$$

$$= \sqrt{309.44}$$

$= 17.6$ correct to 1 decimal place

Example

For the previous example, what percentages of scores lies within one standard deviation of the mean?

Solution

$\bar{x} + \sigma = 61.4 + 17.6 = 79$

$\bar{x} - \sigma = 61.4 - 17.6 = 43.8$

There are six scores that lie within this range.

∴ percentage of scores that lie within one standard deviation

$= \dfrac{6}{10} = 60\%$.

Dependent events

Two or more events are **dependent** if the incidence of one event affects the probability of the other event.

Example

A bag contains three blue marbles and six green marbles. Two marbles are chosen without replacement. Find the probability of choosing one blue and one green marble.

Solution

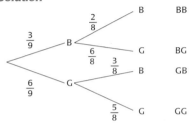

P(one blue and one green) = P(BG) + P(GB)

$$= \frac{3}{9} \times \frac{6}{8} + \frac{6}{9} \times \frac{3}{8}$$

$$= \frac{18}{72} + \frac{18}{72} = \frac{36}{72} = \frac{1}{2}$$